Taming The Fire Within

LIFE AFTER WAR

Anne Freund, Ph.D.

Taming The Fire Within: Life After War

Publishers Note: The information in this book is for educational purposes only. It is not intended to replace the advice of a physician or mental health practitioner. Please see your health care provider before beginning any new health program. The information offered in this book is general and is offered with no guarantees on the part of the publisher or the author. The publisher and author disclaim all liability in connection with the use of this book. The names and identifying information associated with the people or events described in this book have been changed. Any similarity to actual persons, living or dead, or events is coincidental.

The views expressed in this book do not necessarily represent those of the Department of Veterans Affairs or the United States government. Use of Department of Defense images from Defense imagery.mil, on the cover and within the book, do not constitute or imply DoD endorsement.

Bravehearts Books Publishing, L.L.C.
P.O. Box 357216 • Gainesville, FL 32635-7216
WWW.TamingTheFireWithin.com

First Paperbook Edition, printed in the United States of America

Library of Congress Cataloging-in-Publication Data on file

ISBN 978-0-615-39862-4

Bravehearts Books are available at special discounts for bulk purchases by institutions, corporations, or other organizations.

TABLE OF CONTENTS

This book is dedicated to all men and women who have experienced the horrors of war. Thank you for your service, and welcome home.

POW's Returning from Vietnam, 1973, National Archives

ACKNOWLEDGMENTS

This book would not have been possible without the support and encouragement of the following people. My parents, Gerhard and Marion Freund, who gave me a priceless education and have always provided the best example of blazing their own trails through perseverance and determination. My daughter and proofreader, Amy, is a person I truly admire for her strength of spirit and character. She has always been wise beyond her years. Greg Bakeman provided the daily encouragement, shoulder to lean on, and cheerleading necessary for a project like this. I am indebted to my creative consultants, Marie Marshall, Trevor Byrne, Pete Helow, Valerie Seixas, Jodi Stout and Molly. For comedic relief, at just the right times, I thank my brother Michael Freund, Ph.D. and my friend Lori Orme, L.I.S.W. Thanks for invaluable advice go to George Shorter, Ph.D., Kevin McCarthy, Ph.D., and Jan and Brian. Thank you to Ann Landes, Ph.D., Matt Neibaur, M.D. and Lt. Col. (Ret.) Dave Grossman, Jack, Dave, and John for their input. I say a grateful thank you to all of the above.

A special thank you to Paul Stephanus, who generously shared his own, and Robert Ellison's, incredible images of war which so eloquently visually convey the true universal cost of war. Robert Ellison died at Khe Sahn, so the publication of his images is a tribute to his memory. Special thanks to all the photographers who captured the images in this book.

God has used me as a tool to be able to share my vision with some of those who need and deserve it the most. Karma is a good thing. What goes around comes around in the end.

Introduction
by Lt. Col. Dave Grossman

You hold in your hands a vital tool for survival.

I am on the road almost 300 days a year, training warriors to prepare for combat. I teach the FBI, the DEA, the Texas Rangers and the Army Rangers, LAPD SWAT, the SEALS, and the Special Forces. I have filled up the base theaters at Camp LeJeune, Fort Bragg, Coronado, Camp Pendleton, Fort Campbell, Norfolk, Fort Drum, 29 Palms, Fort Polk and many other military bases. My books, *On Killing* and *On Combat* are required reading at many military and law enforcement training centers.

My work has been found to be of value to warriors of every stripe, from every organization.

And I take whatever credibility that gives me and I put it all on the line to tell you again: This book is vital to your survival.

In World War II we lost over 400,000 dead, including every battle and non-battle casualty. But in World War II we also lost over 500,000 psychiatric casualties to psychological wounds! In World War I, World War II, and Korea, the number of soldiers pulled out of the front lines because they were psychiatric casualties was greater than the number of those who died in combat. And many more had to fight mental and emotional battles with post traumatic stress *after* the war.

If it happened to them, could it happen to us?

We are no better than them, but we *can* be better trained, and we *can* be better equipped. Just as we can be prepared to handle the demands of battle with state-of-the-art training and equipment, we can be trained and equipped to survive the aftermath. *That* is what this book is about.

You have spent countless years learning to survive the actual battle. Endless days on the range. Countless hours in battle drills. Months in combat training learning the 'ropes.' Physical fitness training every day. *All* of these were dedicated to ensuring your survival and victory at the moment of truth.

Now, can you dedicate some time to surviving the aftermath? *That* is the purpose of this book, and *that* is why this book is vital to your well-being and survival.

Not just *your* well-being, but that of your loved ones as well.

The psychological scars of war are sometimes called 'The gifts that keeps on giving.' If you die, that's not contagious. But if you come back with a load of mental baggage, then your loved ones will have to live with it!

But it doesn't *have* to be that way. Just as we can equip ourselves to physically survive combat, *so* we can also prepare ourselves to mentally survive the aftermath.

- Reading this book ahead of time can be a form of inoculation, giving you insight that will help you take your combat responses in perspective, avoiding PTSD (Post-traumatic Stress Disorder) at the moment of truth.
- Reading this book after your combat experience is vital to helping you understand what is happening to your mind and body *after* the fact.

And one of the great things about this book is that it applies not just to veterans of our current conflicts, but to *all* veterans of violence, in *every* profession, across the years...

No pity party, no macho man.

First, Do *not* cop a 'Pity Party.'

Try to put your psychological reactions into perspective. Yes, hundreds of thousands of soldiers in World War II were psychiatric casualties. And hundreds of thousands more brought home some mental baggage. But *millions* of them were just fine. They were *all* changed, but most of them went on to lead full, rich lives.

Indeed, *most* veterans are *better* for their experiences. They went on to be "The Greatest Generation."

Do not create an expectation that you will get PTSD. (That can be a self-fulfilling prophecy!) Create an expectation that you will be *just fine*. And reading this book will help to make that so. Psychologists call this, Post-Traumatic Growth. Everyone has heard of PTSD, but not everyone knows about Post-Traumatic Growth.

Nietzsche said, "What does not kill me only makes me stronger." But the Bible says the same thing, over and over again in talking about how we can grow from our trials and tribulations. In Romans, Chapter Five, the Bible says: "We glory in tribulations also: knowing that tribulation worketh patience; and patience, experience; and experience, hope; and hope maketh not ashamed."

People who never have anything go wrong in their lives can be shallow, fragile individuals. It is those who have had challenges and trials in their life, and *grown* from them, who can be strongest in future life challenges. As a combat veteran *you* have had great challenges and tribulations, and you should have an *expectation* that you will be better for your experiences.

This book will help to make that possible.

But, do not be a 'Macho Man' (Or a 'Macho Woman'!). One veteran police officer who survived a shooting experience told me,

> *"Colonel, you tell all these young guys, 'Don't try to be a macho man.' Tell 'em to get help if they need it. I tried to macho it out after my shooting and didn't get help when I needed it, and it damned near killed me. For two years my family and I lived in hell. My wife, my kids, my job: I was losing everything I loved. Finally, just before the divorce, my wife convinced me to get counseling. Two months later it was all over! Two years of pure hell! For me and my family, and I could have ended it any time. You tell 'em, 'Don't be the macho man.'"*

Seeking help, and recognizing the effects of trauma is not a sign of weakness, it is a sign of strength, resilience, and wisdom! No sane person would turn down antibiotics if the doctor prescribed them, and no reasonable warrior should turn away from psychological help if it is available and needed.

This book will help make that possible!

Can you do that? Can you weave a path between the Pity Party and the Macho Man? *That* is what this book is about.

A truly qualified author.

Anne Freund is truly qualified to write this book. Her bio can be found elsewhere, but what is important to know here is that she is eminently qualified, and she has passed the ultimate test: As a Veterans Administration psychologist, across many years, many, many veterans have trusted themselves to her, and she has helped to lead them to a better place.

This is what Medal of Honor recipient Robert Ingram had to say about Dr. Freund's book:

> *"I feel this book will be a good read for the veteran, the family and interested friends. This book should be a beginning to build an understanding that the psychological effects of war are not diseases, but an acquired condition that can be understood and made better with knowledge and self control. You will never forget, but you can learn skills to make it easier to live with. This book will help you gain that knowledge and understanding. Don't punish or exclude your loved ones. Let them be a part of your support group. With God's help you can make a seemingly negative experience into a positive learning event. There is hope. Please know that you are not alone. Semper Fi!"*

Robert "Doc" Ingram, Former Navy Corpsman and Medal of Honor Recipient, Vietnam.

Finally, if you care (and you must!)...

Finally, let me say, if you are a serving warrior or a veteran: *Thank you* for your service!

Or, if you are a loved one of a veteran, or someone who cares, then permit me to say *thank you* for caring.

In either case, if you care (and you *must*!), then don't just read this book. *Study* it! It is vital to your survival, and the well-being of your loved ones.

And you, above all people, have earned the right to live a full, rich, healthy life!

> *"He who did well in war just, earns the right*
> *To begin doing well in peace."*
> Robert Browning

Dave Grossman
Lt. Col. USA (ret.)
Author of *On Killing* and *On Combat*

LT. COL. DAVE GROSSMAN, U.S. ARMY (RET.)
Director, Killology Research Group
870.931.5172 voice • 870.931.3077 fax
www.killology.com

Lt. Col. Dave Grossman is an internationally recognized scholar, author, soldier, and speaker who is one of the world's foremost experts in the field of human aggression and the roots of violence and violent crime.

Col. Grossman is a West Point psychology professor, Professor of Military Science, and an Army Ranger who has combined his experiences to become the founder of a new field of scientific endeavor, which has been termed "killology." In this new field Col. Grossman has made revolutionary new contributions to our understanding of killing in war, the psychological costs of war, the root causes of the current "virus" of violent crime that is raging around the world, and the process of healing the victims of violence, in war and peace.

He is the author of *On Killing*, which was nominated for a Pulitzer Prize; has been translated into Japanese, Korean, and German; is on the US Marine Corps' recommended reading list; and is required reading at the FBI academy and numerous other academies and colleges. Col. Grossman co-authored *Stop Teaching Our Kids to Kill: A Call to Action Against TV, Movie and Video Game Violence*, which has been translated into Norwegian and German, and has received international acclaim. Col. Grossman's most recent book is *On Combat*, the long awaited sequel to *On Killing*.

Col. Grossman has been called upon to write the entry on "Aggression and Violence" in the *Oxford Companion to American Military History*, three entries in the *Academic Press Encyclopedia of Violence* and numerous entries in scholarly journals, to include the *Harvard Journal of Law and Public Policy*.

He has presented papers before the national conventions of the American Medical Association, the

American Psychiatric Association, the American Psychological Association, and the American Academy of Pediatrics.

He has presented to over 40 different colleges and universities world wide.

He has been an expert witness and consultant in state and Federal courts, to include serving on the prosecution team in *United States* vs. *Timothy McVeigh.*

He helped train mental health professionals after the Jonesboro school shootings, and he was also involved in counseling or court cases in the aftermath of the Paducah, Springfield, and Littleton school shootings.

He has testified before U.S. Senate and Congressional committees and numerous state legislatures, and he and his research have been cited in a national address by the President of the United States.

Col. Grossman is an Airborne Ranger infantry officer, and a prior-service sergeant and paratrooper, with a total of over 23 years experience in leading U.S. soldiers worldwide. He retired from the Army in February 1998 and has devoted himself full-time to teaching, writing, speaking, and research. Today he is the director of the Killology Research Group, and in the wake of the 9/11 terrorist attacks he is on the road almost 300 days a year, training elite military and law enforcement organizations worldwide about the reality of combat.

FOREWORD

I wrote this book for veterans of war to help them gain a better understanding of their reactions and experiences after leaving the war zone. I hope those who read this book will understand that their reactions are natural and normal, given the traumatic experiences they have had. As a result, I hope they come to understand that there is no cause for shame in experiencing these reactions. My ultimate wish is to attempt to erase the stigma associated with the psychological reactions to war. It's time to break the silence and be able to talk openly about the natural reactions warriors have when they return home from the war zone. I also wish to raise public awareness of the price that warriors and their families pay in the service of our country. Our country should support our warriors as individuals, even if they do not agree with the politics of the particular war.

This book is written for war veterans of all generations, because the effects of war on the human psyche have been virtually the same since time began. Ancient Greek plays demonstrated the harsh affects of wars on the people who fought them. The photos in this book are from several different time periods. When you look at them you will see the similarities in the actions, emotions, reactions, and the price paid by the warriors involved. Whether a battle is called a "war" or a "conflict" is immaterial. The consequences, in terms of the human toll, are the same. The effects of combat are universal, regardless of the time period or country in which the war is fought. It's this generation's obligation to speak the truth and talk openly about the natural effects of the horrors of war.

I have tried to write this book in a very down to earth way, in a conversational tone, so the reader will feel as if they are sitting across the table from me. There are many wonderful books already written about Post Traumatic Stress Disorder (PTSD) that include therapeutic exercises and worksheets. My purpose is not to recreate those self-help books which are more therapeutic in nature. My goal is to educate the reader about the complex aspects of his or her reactions to war. The tone is purposely non-clinical so that it will be easy to digest.

In coining the phrase "Post Combat Reaction" I hope to raise awareness about the common and natural reactions experienced by all combat veterans to one degree or another. Research shows that that the majority of warriors do not meet the criteria for Post-Traumatic Stress Disorder. Therefore, it is time that we have a way to describe these natural psychological reactions without the stigma of the term "disorder." Hopefully this will help our society to move towards shedding the stigma and shame which has been previously experienced by those seeking help in dealing with their post combat reactions.

The opinions expressed in this book are my own which have developed over the course of my own clinical experiences. They are not a substitute for advice or opinions your own healthcare provider may have shared with you. This book is my personal attempt at obtaining a better understanding about how most, but not all, warriors react and cope with their lives after war. My opinions and explanations will not apply to *everyone* who reads this book. Each person's journey is different. It is my hope that this book will help to begin an open dialogue between war veterans and their families and providers.

As we learn more about the experiences and consequences of war, we have come to understand more fully the toll that is taken on everyone whose lives it touches. We are focusing more on research to better understand what causes the psychological and physical reactions to the severe stressors of the war zone. As research teaches us more, we hope to learn better ways to assist our warriors in their adjustment to life after war. There is a ripple effect on warriors' families and our society as they return from war. It is in our nation's best interest to gain a better understanding of how we can better support our warriors as they return.

Each war has its own unique characteristics which affect each generation. The Vietnam War resulted in a division within our society between those who supported it and those who opposed it. The warriors who actually fought the war were stuck in the middle. Many were treated disrespectfully when they returned home. This caused a tremendous amount of pain, feelings of betrayal, and isolation. This resulted in most of the Vietnam veterans avoiding talking about their experiences. Those years of silence were costly and resulted in an unusually high number of cases of PTSD. Our society, government, and military have responded in much better ways to today's wars in Iraq and Afghanistan in hopes of preventing such a large degree of psychological damage. It is my hope that this book will help to contribute to that goal in some small way. The recent multiple deployments have resulted in an increased toll on today's generation of warriors and an even greater need to be able to talk openly about the effects of war without passing judgments.

The start of the wars in Iraq and Afghanistan re-ignited many of the Vietnam veterans' experiences from their own war. Additionally, many of the Vietnam veterans have retired, providing more time to think about their war experiences. Fortunately, many of them are taking the bull by the horns and coming forward to get help for themselves through the V.A. It has been inspiring to see the camaraderie experienced by these warriors in the PTSD discussion groups. The groups have resulted in these veterans learning about why they've felt the way they have for so many years. They also feel less isolated and are healing some of the wounds caused by society's reaction when they came home. Knowledge is power, and those who have learned more about their reactions to war have been able to ease their burdens a little bit. There is much healing to be done as we help several generations of warriors cope with their lives after war. Today's returning warriors are taking advantage of this ever-growing base of knowledge and information in an attempt to avoid more long term effects.

I have to write a disclaimer here. I've never been to war, or even a war zone, so I don't pretend to even begin to know what the experience is *really* like. However, I do talk every day to those who have been to war. The men and women warriors who have trusted me enough to share their experiences are the ones who have made it possible for me to write this book. Without their willingness to take a risk and talk about their own personal war, none of the assistance I've been able to give to others would be possible. It is you to whom this book is dedicated, with sincere admiration and respect for your courage and strength. Thank you, and welcome home.

Anne Freund, Ph.D.

Taming The Fire Within
LIFE AFTER WAR

Chapter One

Freedom Is Not Free

War is hell. That's why most people don't want to talk about it after they get home. That's why it infuriates you when somebody asks you a really stupid question like "How many people did you kill?" If they understood the full implications of what they were really asking, they wouldn't dare. But there's really no way anyone can fully understand what war is like if they haven't been there. Most war veterans can feel a certain sense of disconnect from civilians, because it's hard to relate to other people who haven't been through the experiences you have. There's no way they could possibly comprehend the intensity, the horror, the fear, the surreal nature of the experiences, sights, sounds, smells. And the ironic thing is that they don't even realize how lucky they are that they don't have these memories, images, or sounds burned into their brains. Ignorance *really is* bliss sometimes. "The taste of freedom will never be fully appreciated by those who haven't fought for it."

On the other hand, they will never know the complete meaning of terms like camaraderie, loyalty, or brotherhood that are experienced on the battlefield. There is no greater love for another human being than being willing to put your life on the line for him or her. This can be one of the best things that comes out of war. Combat brings out the best and the worst of people at a level of intensity that most will never know. Unfortunately, those tight knit bonds are some of the things that are missing after you come home from the war zone. This is true particu-

Vietnam, 1965, AP Photo/Horst Faas

larly when you leave the military. After you get back, who's going to watch your back? I mean *really* watch your back? If you're lucky, you have a few buddies you kept in touch with, but usually everybody is just trying to get back to their lives and deal with the daily grind. So, it's easy to lose touch. It's just not the same. Even your spouse doesn't *truly* understand, although hopefully he or she tries to.

WW I machine gunners in France, 1918, National Archives

So there you are, alone with your memories. You don't want to talk about it and don't really have anybody with whom to discuss your experiences with. Besides, even if you wanted to talk about this with somebody, how would you start that conversation? That's why I wrote this book. So you will know that you are not alone. So you will know that almost every warrior who's been in battle does experience some of the things discussed in this book, to one degree or another, whether they want to admit it or not. Historical documents show that warriors have experienced the harsh effects of combat since the

Combat Outpost Munoz, Afghanistan, 2009, Dept. of Defense

times of the Romans and the Greeks. When people say "war is hell," part of that hell is the after effects you have to live with.

The mental health community frequently refers to the reactions and symptoms war veterans have after the trauma of combat as PTSD (post-traumatic stress disorder). This diagnosis is usually given to combat veterans whose reactions to trauma are so significant that they interfere with their ability to function in several areas of their lives. Severe symptoms of PTSD usually interfere with a person's family relationships, functioning on the job, and even his or her health. Many veterans and civilians are familiar with the term PTSD, but the definitions and symptoms are provided more in depth in Chapter 23. My personal view is that there should be a term for the natural reactions that virtually all warriors have after experiencing the stress and trauma of war. These may not be incapacitating in nature, but definitely have an impact on their lives after they return from the war zone. I would propose that we refer to the set of natural reactions described in this book as "Post Combat Reaction." As you will learn in this book, from both the words

Sniper in Fallujah, Iraq, 2004, Dept. of Defense

and the photographs, all warriors experience virtually the same reactions to war. I hope that providing a name for these universal reactions will help to alleviate the stigma or shame sometimes associated with PTSD.

Military culture demands that warriors "suck it up and press on." Combat requires that. There is no time for grieving the loss of your friend or being able to process some of the horrors you may have witnessed. If you lose focus on the mission, you or somebody else could die. You have to maintain high alert status 24/7 while you're in the war zone. You have to make sure that orders are followed immediately and correctly, or people could die. There is no time to stop and weigh the pros and cons when you are confronted with a threat. You have to respond aggressively and immediately, or there could be more casualties. All these reactions become reflexes and instincts. These reflexes become even more deeply ingrained the younger you are when you learn them. These kinds of reactions and learned responses are not something you can just turn off like a light switch when you get home from war. They are necessary for your survival in war, but sometimes don't sit too well with family members or other civilians after you get home.

So what happens after you come home from war or leave the military? It's pretty surreal for most folks. I've talked to guys who were literally in a firefight on their last day in Vietnam, only to be sitting at their Mom's kitchen table in Ohio within 72 hours. Or guys who came home from deployment in Iraq and had to go back to their office job within a week. What, are you freakin' kidding me?!! Even police dogs get some kind of debriefing, period of time after they retire if they're going to stay with the law enforcement officer's family. They do it for dogs, but they don't do it for humans? Somehow you're just supposed to magically adapt to life as you knew it before war? It's not that easy. War changes people in a big way. But the people who were back at home didn't go through those changes. They went through many changes of their own, but not the same ones you did. And somehow everybody is supposed to try to reconnect and carry on, business as usual? Not so much.

As you read this book, look carefully at the photographs from the various war zones. One of the things you will probably notice is how similar the images are,

Afghanistan door to door, 2004, Dept. of Defense

DaNang, Vietnam, National Archives

regardless of what time period they are from. The uniforms and weapons may be different, but the faces and the emotions portrayed are virtually the same. Another thing you may notice is how young the people are. Many people go to war when they're only 18-21 years old. In the overall scheme of a person's life, that's pretty young. The good news is that young people are resilient, strong, enthusiastic, and willing to follow orders. The not so good news is that young people are still growing. They are more impressionable, less experienced, and more easily influenced. The experiences young people have in war are more likely to affect their future development, as compared with those who are older and more fully developed. This is why so many of the habits and reflexes developed in a war zone are so likely to carry over into civilian life afterwards. Things we learn when we're young tend to stay with us and to be more easily ingrained into our personality. This is especially true when those reactions, beliefs, behaviors, and reflexes are developed during life or death situations. The likelihood of having them become deeply ingrained is even greater

Khe Sahn, Vietnam, 1968, Robert Ellison/Empire News

when the stakes and consequences are so high. That's why the reactions most people have after having been in a combat zone are natural and normal given what they've been through. There is no shame or stigma in that.

The images in this book really convey the experiences people have in a war zone. They capture some of the intensity, exhaustion, fear, sadness, loneliness, anger, helplessness, frustration, loyalty, brotherhood, and camaraderie which develop in combat. As you see the emotions in the pictures, hopefully it will provide an objective portrayal which shows that everybody does, indeed, experience similar reactions. War is hell. The photographs show it clearly. That's why nobody goes unscathed. Nobody.

It's time to break the silence and admit the reality. The reality is that all warriors return from war with emotional battle scars of some kind. It's time to acknowedge this reality and get rid of the stigma. It is what it is. So let's call it "Post Combat Reaction" (PCR) so that the average warrior's reactions are not called a "disorder."

Hue City, Vietnam, 1968, National Archives

CHAPTER TWO

The Only Easy Day Was Yesterday

Combat thrusts people into some of the most horrific and potentially traumatic events known to mankind. Nothing can fully prepare you for what you will experience in war. The civilized façade is stripped away to expose the most primitive aspects of human behavior. People are thrown into situations in which they make split second life or death decisions, the results of which they will have to live with for the rest of their lives. This is a daunting task for even the most experienced, hardened individual, let alone for the young and relatively inexperienced. The chaos and intensity of combat, combined with the adrenalin, fear and anger can cause people to do things they would never do in

Khe Sahn, Vietnam, 1968, Robert Ellison/Empire News

regular civilian circumstances. Sometimes warriors feel as if they are observing themselves going through the motions, as if it's unreal. Many people describe combat as an almost surreal experience in which their senses can become distorted. Time may seem to stand still or speed up. All of these factors cause difficulties when you try to make sense of some of the experiences you've had after the fact.

War results in death, pain, and suffering for virtually all those involved. These things are to be expected in war. However, these experiences are traumatic for most people. When you are wounded or almost killed, it is traumatic. Death may be considered a natural part of the life cycle. However, violent, sudden death is unacceptable, particularly if it involves the deaths of young people. The young are not supposed to die before the old. It doesn't make sense in the cycle of life. Even though

Ia Drang Valley, Vietnam, 1965, National Archives

death and getting wounded are expected parts of war, they aren't any easier to accept or make sense of. Even animals become agitated and upset when one of their own kind is wounded or killed. It's a very primal reaction which most species experience at one level or another. Humans experience it to an even greater degree because of our ability to empathize and think about the ramifications of death and human suffering.

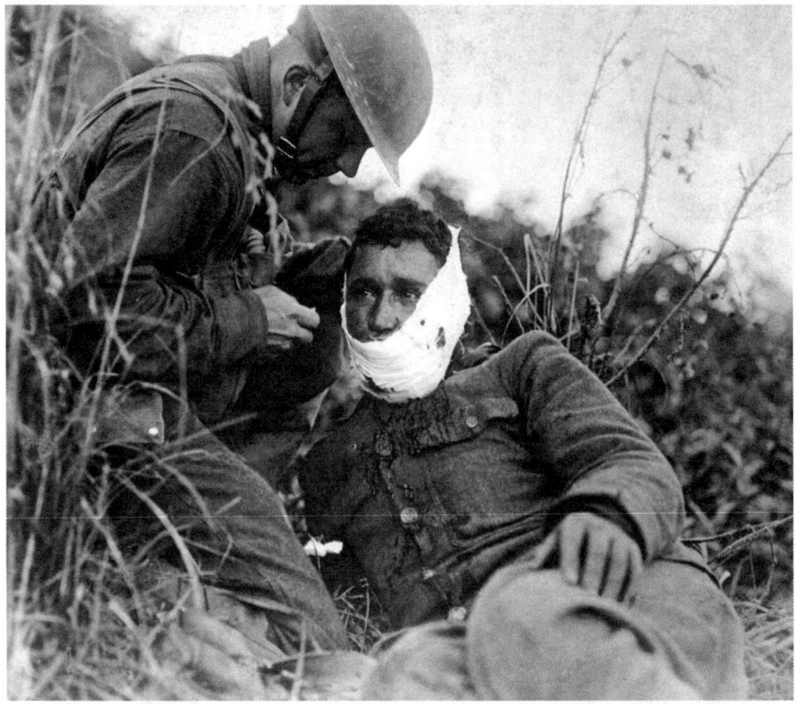

WW I Wounded Marine in France,1915, National Archives

People can experience trauma in war when they witness somebody die, take another human's life, or are wounded themselves. In cases like that, it is considered a "primary" trauma if you are directly involved in some way. A "secondary" trauma exposure is when you witness something traumatic happening to somebody else. You may see it, hear it over a radio, or see the aftermath. Anything that causes you horror or is life threatening is considered to be traumatic. People can also experience "vicarious" trauma when they hear about another person's traumatic experiences. I've spoken to people who have been more traumatized by listening helplessly over a radio as their friends were ambushed than when they themselves were in a firefight. I've heard people describe how horrible and difficult it was to have to notify a family that their loved one was killed in action.

My Tho, Vietnam, 1968, National Archives

For most people who experience a trauma in civilian life, it is a single episode. Hopefully, afterwards they are surrounded by sympathetic people who will support them and keep them safe. They may be able to talk about what just happened to them and even take time off from work. They usually have an opportunity to begin the natural healing process of coming to terms with what has happened to them. However, in war the traumas usually occur on a continuous basis in an unsafe environment. It is impossible to begin the natural healing process when your life is still in danger and more traumatic events are occurring, adding additional layers of trauma. For example, the grunt in the field often has constant trauma exposure and a high level of danger and possible death. Perhaps you just saw your buddy killed or wounded, so you know you could be next.

Rooftop in Fallujah, Iraq, 2004, Dept. of Defense

You're on high alert status, so you can't stop long enough to psychologically process or make sense of what you've just experienced. You're already anticipating the next traumatic event and just trying to stay alive.

As a result, most warriors describe going through stages when they're in combat. Unless something traumatic happens to them early on, they frequently feel somewhat invincible in the beginning. You figure "getting shot is something that happens to other people, not me." That feeling of invulnerability comes to a screeching halt the first time you witness somebody get killed or wounded, or get wounded yourself. All of a sudden, death becomes a reality, and then pure unadulterated terror and fear can set in. After feeling so much fear, the emotional response system can get overloaded and shut down. That's when you may become numb and detached. You begin to think, "It don't mean a thing." Then the exhaustion can set in.

Afghanistan door to door, 2010, Dept. of Defense

You may have gotten to the point where you accepted the fact that you were probably going to die, so you almost didn't even care anymore. You may have adopted an "I'm never gonna make it out of this place alive, so screw it" attitude. However, when you become a "short timer" and realize you may actually have a chance of making it home alive, you start to get scared again. Hope resurfaces. That's when the fear comes back again, because you're so close, yet so far away from making it out of this hell hole. You might actually get to see your family again. During that last month in theatre, if you haven't made contact with the enemy, you might almost wish it would happen so you can go ahead and get it over with. That's a very unpleasant roller-coaster ride by anybody's standards.

Khe Sahn, Vietnam, 1968, Robert Ellison/Empire News

Vietnam, Used with permission from Stars and Stripes. Copyright Stars and Stripes

You can see the complexity and variety of traumas that war involves. No wonder these experiences have long lasting effects after the fact. Warriors have to get very good at being able to control their emotions and reactions in combat. The coping skills you develop in war are multifaceted and complicated. The good news, is that they help you survive the hell of war. The not so good news, is that the coping skills required in war may be misunderstood on the home front by those who haven't been to war. This gap in experiences and coping skills between you and your family can be bridged by open communication. In order to be able to explain your post combat reactions (PCR) to your loved ones, you have to acquire the knowledge yourself first. This book is designed to provide you with the information you need to understand your own reactions better, and in turn be able to communicate with your family and friends. Knowledge is power.

In war, you had to learn how to cope with all the different types of trauma on your own. Nobody taught you or prepared you for how to react or cope with the horrors you may experience in combat. As a result, you did the best you could given the difficult situations you were thrust into. Once you've learned these coping skills during war, they are likely to stay with you for the rest of your life. You've developed tremendous strengths and effective coping skills for dealing with war. This book will help you learn how to better integrate these strengths and coping skills into your life after war.

Desert Shield, 1991, Dept. of Defense

Chapter Three

High Speed Low Drag

How are you supposed to go from "high speed, low drag" to "Daddy/Mommy" or "Mr./Mrs. So-And-So" on the job? I've heard many people say they miss the adrenalin, excitement, power, control, responsibility, authority and camaraderie they had over there. It's pretty hard to go from 100 mph in a war zone to 25 mph in a school zone. It's hard to go from kicking in doors, firing weapons, jumping out of helicopters, or taking over villages to making someone do their homework or listening to them complain about traffic on the way to work.

Iraq Combat Reaction Team, 2004, Dept. of Defense

Grenade launcher in Iraq, 2004, Dept. of Defense

It's like trying to take an engine that's used to revving at high speed and trying to throttle it back suddenly. It takes some conscious effort to accomplish it. A typical example of somebody trying to throttle back is as follows. A teenager took his Dad's screwdriver off his work bench and didn't put it back. Well, when Dad found the screwdriver was missing, he went ballistic! Junior thinks "Dad is being a jerk again!" But what he doesn't realize is that in Iraq, Dad was responsible for making sure the helicopter was good to go to pick up Special Forces teams. That's an example of when a missing screwdriver can be a matter of life or death over there in the war zone. Dad wonders why he's "over-reacting" when everybody else in the family is looking at him like he's crazy. However, in the recent past, if that screwdriver wasn't where it should be, it had the potential to have the most serious, ultimate consequences. This exemplifies why some of those misunderstandings occur so often with family members once you get home.

Iraq rooftop extraction, 2004, Dept. of Defense

So, the first step in readjusting is that you recognize that the "little things" you're getting upset about, often times, aren't such "little things" at all. Usually, when somebody gets that upset about something, there's a valid reason. Often times it's not that obvious on the surface why they're getting so upset. But if you look a little deeper, you're likely to find out what that reason is. Talking to your family about why this "little thing" is such a big deal to you can certainly help calm the tensions a little bit.

Identifying your triggers is extremely important. When I say triggers, I'm talking about the things from the war zone which could have meant danger or were associated with a traumatic event you experienced. For most people, those triggers have to do with their five senses. For example, it might be hearing something, like a helicopter. Almost anybody who's been in a war zone has an emotional reaction to the sound or sight of a helicopter. It means somebody's coming to haul your ass out, or to bring help. Or maybe it meant you were about to

Ia Drang Valley, Vietnam, 1966, National Archives

be dropped off in a place where you really didn't want to be. Either way there's usually some kind of emotion like relief or fear. Hearing a loud boom or gunfire may make you hit the deck. That kind of reaction can be annoying or embarrassing if there are other people around. On the other hand, you really don't want to totally lose your ability to respond to that kind of attack automatically without thinking. It could save your life.

Back in civilian life, whenever you see or hear a helicopter, it's likely to trigger the same emotions or reactions it did from when you were in the war zone. It's also likely to trigger memories along with the emotions. Some of those memories may be good, but many of them may also be very bad. It can help take the edge off a little if you know what triggered your memory and emotion. By identifying the trigger, at least you can usually exert some control over how often you're exposed to that trigger. Or else be a little bit more prepared for your reaction the next time you encounter it.

Attack on Pearl Harbor, Hawaii, 1941, National Archives

Another example of a trigger might be a smell, like diesel fuel or something burning. Smell can be one of the most powerful triggers for eliciting memories. In most war zones, something burning has real significance (unless of course it's latrine-related). It might be a village or a vehicle or something worse. Maybe it was something set on fire on purpose to accomplish a mission. Maybe accomplishing that mission had emotions associated with it, either good or bad. Maybe something blew up and caught on fire by accident. Either way, the smell of something burning is likely to trigger some kind of feelings of disgust, fear, regret, guilt, sadness, or maybe even relief.

Khe Sahn, Vietnam, 1968, Robert Ellison/Empire News

If you live in a hot or tropical climate, like the south, the sensation of the heat and humidity is likely to serve as a trigger. Whether it's the jungles of Vietnam or the deserts of Iraq, it might have the same physical sensation, which can serve as a trigger. Maybe that sensation reminds you of the crappy day-to-day dampness or heat and sweat. Maybe it reminds you of a dangerous ambush or a day of R&R (rest and relaxation). Either way, there's likely to be an emotion attached to it, just like with the other triggers. Anybody who was in Vietnam or possibly Afghanistan or Panama will tell you that having several days of rain causes an emotional reaction. It brings back the same feelings associated with monsoon season or flooding or rain forests.

Vietnam, 1967, Paul Stephanus, Empire News

Who hasn't tasted something that reminded them of an MRE (meal ready to eat) or C-rations (canned prepared meal), or smelled something cooking that reminded you of the locals in your war zone? The taste or smell can elicit a very strong reaction. Those who were in Korea said they could smell when the enemy was close from the garlic. There are guys who were in Vietnam who also say they could smell when the enemy was nearby in the jungle.

Then take a look at the foliage around you. Tree lines can cause intense hypervigilance and scanning for the enemy. Tropical foliage can remind you of the jungle.

The sand at the beach can make your skin crawl, since it reminds you of the desert. All of these have the potential to be significant triggers for you.

Napalm South of Saigon, Vietnam, 1965, National Archives

One of the reasons that people's five senses serve as such powerful triggers is because of the primitive level at which the associations are made. Your reaction to a smell or sound is almost like an immediate reflex. If I tell you to think about a lemon, you're likely to start salivating automatically, without even thinking about it.

So, you can see how easily somebody could get blindsided by a trigger. You're out minding your own business and going through your day, when out of nowhere, a trigger pops up. You hear a weapon fired or something that sounds like a mortar. You see a helicopter fly over or smell something burning. Next thing you know, you're feeling irritable or depressed and you're not even sure why. Nothing hugely important has happened over the course of your day, but you still feel like crap. Every little thing gets on your nerves, or you just want to be left alone. You start to wonder "What the hell is wrong with me?" The answer is, "Nothing."

Firing mortars in Iraq, 2004, Dept. of Defense

Having an emotional response to an unpleasant trigger is a natural reaction. You are exposed to the trigger, which in turn sets off the response, like a reflex. Once your body reacts to the trigger, the emotions soon follow, almost automatically. It's like a chain reaction. Trigger, physical response, emotional reaction. And it happens in a split second. Once the emotional reaction occurs, memories are likely to follow. Even if you try to ignore the reaction or emotions, you can't erase it. So, the subconscious mind dredges up the other details of the original trauma or experience. It's like falling dominoes; one reaction sets off the next reaction and the next. So all this reacting and remembering is happening below the surface. Maybe you're aware that it's happening, or maybe you're not. Either way, sometimes this can result in people having difficulty concentrating on a task on which they're working in the present.

On some occasions, a trigger can result in a flashback. A true flashback is when a person actually feels as if they are back in the war zone or in combat. For that

Operation Georgia, Vietnam, 1966, National Archives

moment they lose touch with their present environment and their mind re-enacts the traumatic combat experience. It is a pretty unnerving experience for anybody who's ever had one. It can be surreal, since you're out of touch with your environment and lose track of time in the present. Usually it only lasts a few seconds or so. If you're having true flashbacks, it's a good idea to discuss it with your doctor or counselor. It's not something you should have to go through alone.

Marines in Mogadishu, Somalia, 1992, Dept. of Defense

In general, if you're aware of your triggers and of what's going on in your mind, then you're better off. At least that way, if you're cranky, distracted, irritable or depressed, you know you have a good reason. You've just been thinking about some traumatic event that occurred in the war zone. That's enough to wreck anybody's day. That's powerful, weighty stuff that you didn't have to deal with just before the trigger set you off. Now, you find yourself having to deal not only with the memories, but also the frustration of having your day interrupted by something over which you had no control. That stinks!

One of the most frustrating things about triggers is that you usually can't control when or where they're going to rear their ugly heads. You might be at the park with your family when you smell something burning. You might be out walking your dog when a helicopter flies

Afghanistan checkpoint, 2010, Dept. of Defense

over. You might be doing some yard work when the heat and humidity just takes over. You might be working on an old car when the smell of the mildew sets off a panic attack. The lack of control is extremely frustrating for most people, but particularly for those of you who have been in control of so many things during the war. You're used to being on top of every possible aspect of a situation. You're the ultimate in being prepared for anything which might go wrong. That's because if anything goes wrong or isn't planned for in war, people die. There's no fooling around with leaving things to chance. There are too many factors in war that are beyond your control, so you have to make extra sure you do control the things you can.

Communicate with your family about what your triggers are. There's no way for them to know unless you tell them. Triggers may seem obvious to you, like the helicopter example. But to many people a helicopter has no meaning, other than a mode of transportation or loud sound in the sky. It's up to you to educate your family about what your triggers are and why. That way they can understand you better and understand where some

Bosnia, 1996, Dept. of Defense

of your reactions are coming from. You don't have to go into any gory details about why certain smells, sounds, or situations are horrific to you. For example, hopefully it's enough just to say that whenever a helicopter flew over, it meant some bad or scary things were about to happen. You can educate them at whatever level you think is appropriate for them. Perhaps with your spouse, you might even say that a smell reminds you of death, without going into the specifics. That sure makes it easier for the other person to understand why you went from going along just fine, to acting sullen, withdrawn or irritable. If you don't explain it to them, they're likely to take it personally and react in a negative way. It's much more fair to let them in on what's happening and why.

Iraq, Dept. of Defense

Once you've gotten used to your adrenalin firing on all cylinders for long periods at a time, you can miss it when it's gone. Some people will describe themselves as "adrenalin junkies" and continue to seek out thrilling, adrenalin inducing situations. How many combat veterans take their motorcycle out on the open road at 100 mph or higher for the thrill? How many have other hobbies or activities that qualify as being "thrill seeking?" Some people will even look for fights when they first get home, just to feel the adrenalin high again. It's hard to go from kicking in doors to staying home watching a movie on TV. Some people will tell you they also miss the power, along with the adrenalin. Like I said, it's pretty hard to throttle back after you've been in combat mode. Be patient with yourself and discuss it with your family if you can. It will help them understand you better and hopefully ease the tension.

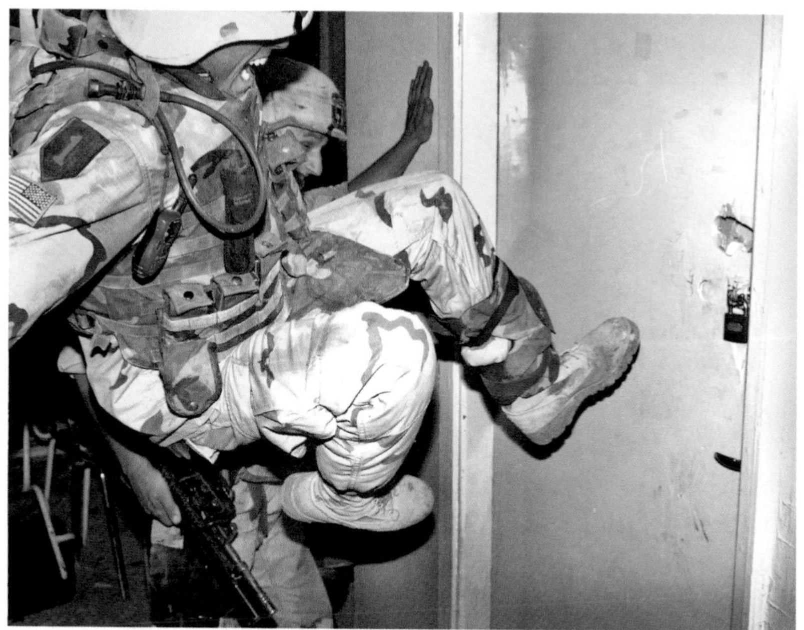

Kicking down doors, Iraq, 2004, Dept. of Defense

CHAPTER FOUR

Stay Alert Stay Alive

Whether you're walking point in a jungle, in a desert, or on a city street, all your senses are on super high alert status. You have to be very focused and alert to every detail. You have to be scanning, analyzing and preparing constantly. You're in full battle rattle and ready to go. Your heart rate may be going up just reading about it. That's how strongly ingrained the survival instinct is. It's pretty hard to pull the throttle back on something like this. Even when you're back in a relatively safe environment like a base or camp, or even back home in the U.S. Once you've had to be at this level of hyperalert status, it's almost impossible to come back down to baseline again. One of the reasons for this is that survival is one of the strongest instincts that all animals have. It's been bred into us. It's in our genes.

Booby trap in tunnel, Vietnam, 1967, Robert Ellison/Empire News

"Preservation of the species." That means, "I will protect myself and my family at all costs." For most people that is an abstract concept that doesn't really mean much. However, once you've been directly in the line of fire and really experienced other people trying to kill you, it ain't so abstract anymore. Having a buddy get killed makes it pretty real, too. Most people can almost pinpoint a particular experience they had in combat when they realized it was the real deal. All of a sudden it became clear that a particular person, or group of people, were trying to kill you. They were shooting real bullets or rockets at you personally. All of a sudden it goes from abstract to horrifying reality. Nothing is ever the same after that. Now all bets are off.

Bringing in a patient, Afghanistan, 2010, Dept. of Defense

From that moment forward you are hypervigilant. Your training has prepared you to be always on guard and to anticipate any possible danger. Your training has also prepared you for how to handle almost every eventuality. You've trained and practiced over and over again so that it becomes second nature. Ever noticed that in any emergency situation, military people, veterans, first responders and healthcare personnel are always the first to spring into action without getting upset? Training. Most civilians, unless they've had emergency training, don't respond as immediately. Likewise, many untrained people don't have the same level of awareness of potential threats and dangers. They usually haven't been trained to scan and analyze situations the same way you have.

Dak To, Vietnam, 1967, National Archives

As a result, you're pretty much on high alert status whenever you're not in your home or a safe place. Even when you're there, you're on a more modified level of alert status. If there's any noise out of the ordinary, you hear it. If anything seems out of place, you investigate it. While you're out in public you're spending a lot of energy on scanning and analyzing the information you're taking in. It's reflex, but it still takes energy that a lot of people don't expend. You're analyzing potential threats and solutions, and planning what you'll do "if something happens." This is great, because you and your family will be safe. Nobody is going to sneak up on you.

You know where all the exits are and like to sit where you can see who's coming and going. You also usually like to sit with your back to the wall. It's more protected. You avoid crowds, because there are so many potential threats to keep track of. It takes a lot of energy and can be exhausting.

Going up a hill, Iraq, 2003, Dept. of Defense

Most people just wake up, get ready, drive on autopilot to, for example, the doctor's office, park the car, walk in, and sign in at the desk. No problem. You, on the other hand, have probably been awake way before you had to get up, if you slept at all. Maybe you had a bad dream and still feel upset. You drag yourself out of bed and get ready. You begin your drive by scanning and analyzing. You're paying attention to the cars in front of you, behind you, on either side of you, and further down the road. You're taking note of the color of the vehicles, how many people are in them, and the fact that the driver is on the cell phone. Your blood pressure goes up. All of this is being filtered through your mind automatically. If you've been in a combat zone in a city, you're scanning the roof tops for snipers or the side of the road for possible IEDs. You're thinking about possible escape and evade routes. Your blood pressure goes up.

American Phillipine War, 1899, National Archives

You may or may not be aware that all of this processing is going on. It may have become so much of a reflex that you're not even aware of it anymore. You see how careless other drivers are and notice some near misses. That makes you angry because it's so unnecessary, and it could kill somebody needlessly. You've probably seen or heard enough of that overseas. That doesn't need to happen here at home too. Your blood pressure goes up a little more. You get to the doctor's office parking lot. You may look for cars which look weighted down, possibly with explosives, or look out of place. Then you walk to the doctor's office, taking note of the people you pass, analyzing them as potential friend or foe. You finally get there, and the person behind the desk doesn't notice you standing there. How could he or she not notice? Your blood pressure goes up a little bit more. Now you get to sit there and wait for your appointment. Why does the person sitting next to you look so calm and peaceful when you feel like you're going to explode? The answer? Hypervigilance. The double-edged sword. You're safe and prepared, but it cost you a lot to be that way.

Somalia, 1993, Dept. of Defense

You have a level of training and awareness that most civilians don't have. You've been through Basic Training and A.I.T. (advanced individual training) and in a war zone. So, naturally, you pay closer attention when you're out in the public sector, particularly when you're driving or going into an unknown place. When somebody cuts you off in traffic, you think to yourself, "They must be doing it on purpose, nobody could be that stupid!" Well, actually… Most civilians, unless they're first responders, aren't trained to scan, analyze, plan and prepare for the worst like those of you with military training are. Most people just pull into a parking lot or walk into a store and don't think much about it. However, anybody with military training scans for potential threats or allies, evaluates and assesses the situation for safety, finds out where the exits are, plans potential escape routes, and is ready for whatever might happen. Even though that's an automatic response for you, it still takes a lot

Iraq, 2004, Dept. of Defense

of energy that most people don't have to use. The good part about that is that you're prepared for anything that might happen and will be able to respond appropriately and immediately. The bad part is that you're tensed up, hyperviligant, locked and loaded, and ready to rock and roll if need be. That takes up a lot of energy and makes you tense. If you layer that on top of not having had a good night's sleep or maybe a nightmare, it's going to tend to make a person cranky.

Awareness of your own reactions is the first step. Once you've identified why you're so tense, the next step is to take a deep breath. Remind yourself that you're not in a war zone anymore. After reassessing your environment, try to throttle back just a little bit to lower your alert status from red to orange, or even yellow. And as always, try to explain your reactions to your family. This will help them better understand why you react the way you do. You might want to let them read this book so they can learn more about it.

Afghanistan, 2010, Dept. of Defense

CHAPTER FIVE

"I Said Do It Now!"

The consequences and stakes in war are very high. The pressure not to make any mistakes is enormous. You don't question an order. You do it immediately, and you better do it right the first time, or people could die. Or you could die. There is no time for hesitation in combat. There is no time to mull over whether the order is correct or whether you agree with it or don't. There is no luxury of debating the merits of doing it his way or your way. You just have to do it and do it NOW. And don't screw it up! So, once again, Dad/Mom gets all bent out of shape when the kids don't do what he/she tells them to do right away. It's true that taking out the garbage right away will not have life or death consequences, unless there's something really nasty in there like toxic waste. But just like many other ways of doing things in war, this is ingrained into the very fiber of your being. It started in boot camp. It's almost like brain washing from the standpoint that it becomes part of who you are and the way you think automatically.

That's the whole point. You're supposed to react automatically in battle. No time to think or question, otherwise you're dead.

So naturally the kids are looking at Dad/Mom like he/she's nuts for going ballistic when they didn't take the garbage out or clean their room when he/she told them to. All Dad/Mom knows is how pissed off he/she is when they don't follow orders. You want to make sure your children

WW II Marine charging a hill in Okinawa, 1945, National Archives

are safe and learn to act immediately if necessary for their own safety. Now you know why it bothers you so much. It's not really about the garbage or the dirty room. It's about a fundamental way of reacting for survival. For you, but not for them. To be fair to them, unless any of them have been in the military, there's really no way they would understand or know the importance of following orders. Besides, they weren't drafted and didn't enlist, so they don't follow the same set of rules and expectations.

This is where talking to your family or co-workers can ease some of the tension. If you explain to them why you react in such a strong fashion, they're likely to be a little more understanding. Of course this is a quid pro quo situation, so you have to try to maintain an awareness that your place of work or home is not a military installation. More importantly, you have to remember that you're not in a war zone anymore. It takes work and effort to keep reminding yourself about this fact. Like I said before, this has truly become not your second nature, but your first nature. You have become this way out of necessity for survival. Self-awareness is the key here. You can't reign yourself in or alter your reaction if

Afghanistan, 2010, Dept. of Defense

you're not aware you're having it, or don't know where it's coming from. Knowledge is power.

Sitting down and talking about this issue frankly with the other folks involved goes a long way. Some families come up with a code word or phrase to remind the veteran that this is the kind of reaction he or she is having. I'm not talking about being critical or saying something embarrassing. You can even use a sense of humor about it. For example, let the family members say "Sir, yes Sir, may I have another Sir,"... even if you're a Ma'am. Come up with some kind of signal that works for you, so your family or co-workers can remind you that this is the civilian world and military rules don't always apply. Find some way to calm yourself down.

Khe Sahn, Vietnam, 1968, Robert Ellison/Empire News

Chapter Six

Danger: High Explosives

"Watch out for him, he's got a hair trigger temper!" I don't know about you, but when I don't get enough sleep I'm pretty cranky. Most people are, particularly if they're sleep deprived for more than a few nights. Most people who have been in a war zone have had to sleep with one ear and one eye open. This is another survival skill. It doesn't just go away once you're home. So if you've had a nightmare and still have the aura or after image of the emotion that went with it, you're likely not to be in the best of moods. Strike one.

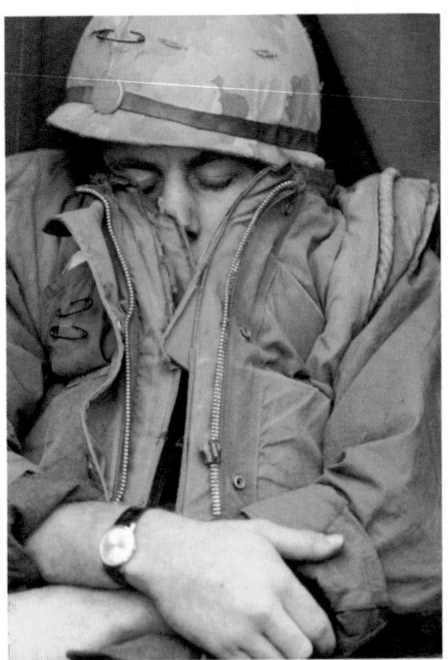

Khe Sahn, Vietnam, 1968, Robert Ellison/Empire News

Strike two is always having to be alert and hypervigilant. As I said before, things like that take a lot of energy that most people don't have to use. If you're on alert status, you're already wound pretty tight. This is particularly true if you have to go to places where there are lots of people or vehicles to keep track of. So you're already pretty tense, which contributes to quick reactions, good or bad.

Korea, 1950, National Archives

Strike three has to do with your training. You are trained to respond to a threat by taking proactive, aggressive action to neutralize the threat or enemy. It's been drilled into you since boot camp. You weren't trained to sit down and "talk" about the conflict with the enemy. You were trained to attack. This doesn't work so well in the civilian world, with family members in particular. It can also cause "inconvenient" situations out in public. Not to mention it might land you in jail. You know what I'm talking about.

Operation New Castle, Vietnam, 1967, National Archives

So is it any wonder that people think you have a quick temper? My guess is that most people would be irritable given those circumstances. Heck, some people are even cranky only because they haven't had their coffee yet, and they haven't even been through the experiences you have. They probably had a decent night's sleep and they,'re still cranky.

I like to call that hair trigger reaction the "threat response system." On the battlefield there is no time to think about how you should react to a threat. Your reaction has to be immediate, decisive, and without hesitation. Hesitation can mean death. All of your training leads up to being prepared to take aggressive, proactive action in response to the threat. If you are being attacked there is no luxury of time to weigh your options and give careful deliberation to all aspects of the situation. This becomes hardwired as a matter of survival. Life or death.

Many people refer to this as the "fight, flight or freeze" response. The body and mind immediately start firing on all cylinders. The adrenalin kicks in, the stress hormones start firing, and the muscles tense up. The body even redirects the blood flow toward your extremities so that you can either fight or run like hell. Sometimes the intensity of the reaction can result in somebody actually freezing up. If this has happened to you, know that this is one of the natural reactions that can occur. It doesn't mean you're a coward or defective in some way. It just happens sometimes. As a result of this threat response system being so active in a war zone, you can't just flip it off like a light switch when you get home. It's still there as a reflex. This is absolutely necessary in a war zone. However, it doesn't always work so well back in the civilian world.

Khe Sahn, Vietnam, 1968, Robert Ellison/Empire News

You are more likely to react strongly to a threat which involves your safety or security, or that of your family's. You are likely to have a very strong proactive reaction in any threatening situation. A good example of this occurs while you are driving. Anybody who cuts you off or is driving carelessly is likely to cause you to react very strongly, probably with anger and aggression. This is the perfect set-up for road rage, particularly if you're used to having to avoid IED's (improvised explosive devices) or mines.

Car bomb, Iraq, 2003, Dept. of Defense

Part of the reason you react so strongly to triggers like this is that people dying is a reality for you. For many civilians, death is an abstract concept. It's something they have read about in books or seen in movies. It's not a part of their reality. However, for you, sudden, violent death is part of your reality. You know all too well how real it is so you're more likely to take potentially dangerous situations much more seriously. Many civilians make the assumption that, "those things only happen to other people, not to me." They may think, "That's not something that really happens to people like us." Unfortunately, you have probably witnessed the reality of young people dying suddenly and violently.

You have a level of awareness and training that most civilians, with the exception of first responders, will never have. You have been trained to scan your environment, analyze what you see, anticipate potential problems, and be prepared for how you will handle the dangerous situation should it arise. This whole analytical process occurs automatically for you, like a reflex. However, it also takes a lot of energy that most people don't have to expend. Most people are just going along assuming everything is okay, unless something tells them otherwise. Once again, ignorance is bliss.

Mine sweeping in Afghanistan, 2010, Dept. of Defense

This is part of why you get so angry when somebody cuts you off in traffic. "Surely nobody could be that stupid!" you think. Well, it's not that they're stupid. They just don't have the level of awareness and training that you have. You're locked and loaded almost all of the time, because you've had to be for your survival. Back home, they haven't had to be at that level of preparedness. There's a huge gap between those two levels of being.

The other thing to know about this threat response system is that it's so automatic that it pretty much goes from 0 to 90 mph instantaneously, particularly when you're at war. The whole system ramps up immediately in order to respond to the threat. As I said before, this frequently carries over into life after you get home. The rapid response of this system is critical in combat, because it means survival. It's important to be aware of all of this so you can monitor yourself.

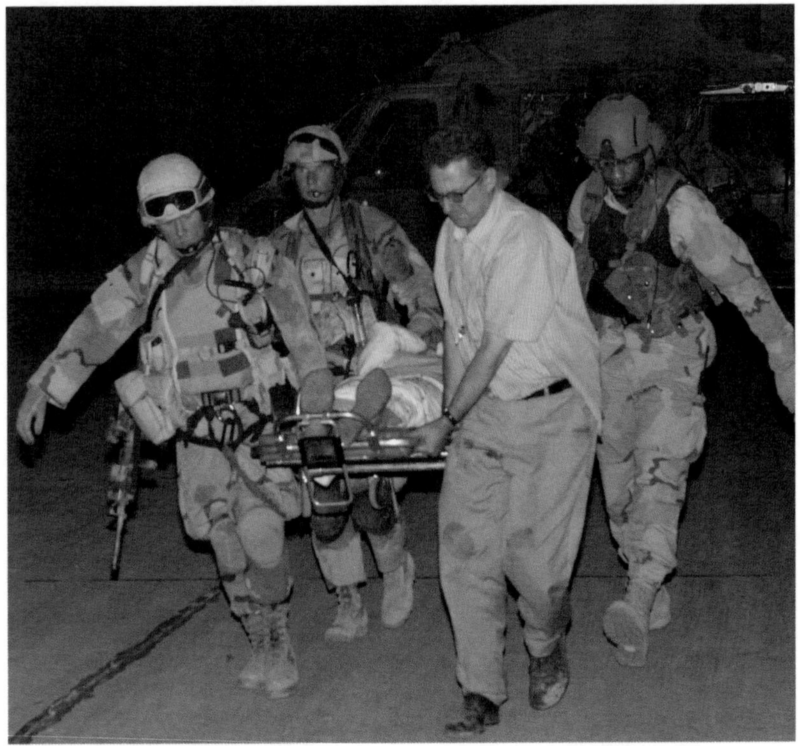

Wounded in Baghdad, 2003, Dept. of Defense

Awareness is the first step. Monitoring your temper takes a lot of energy. That's one of the reasons a lot of war veterans avoid being around other people when they come home. They don't want to go to a family reunion or the grocery store or a restaurant, or anywhere else where there are crowds. Not only are there too many potential threats to monitor, but you also know somebody might do something stupid or threatening to set off your temper. After all, you know what you're capable of if you get provoked or threatened. It isn't always pretty either. This is one reason some veterans will not own guns anymore. They're afraid of what they might do. On the other hand, many veterans insist on having a weapon to protect themselves and their families.

Once you're more aware of your anger, try to identify your triggers. What are the things that usually make you angry? Is it people being disrespectful? Is it people acting "stupid," which usually means acting unaware, inefficient, or careless? Try to figure out as specifically as possible what your triggers are. Once you have identified the situations in which you're most likely to get angry, you can act accordingly. Either you can try to avoid those types of situations, or you can plan ahead for how you're going to respond. Usually, leaving the situation or potential confrontation is the best choice. Many times the consequences of a confrontation will not be worth it. The thought of jail time has kept many a person from taking action or saying what they really wanted to.

Mosul, Iraq, 2004, Dept. of Defense

Learn to identify the signals that you're beginning to get angry. Do you feel your muscles start to tense up or your adrenalin start to flow? Do you feel the anger brewing in your gut? Sometimes people say, "I just see red." However, usually there are some warning signs before it gets to that point. Sometimes people feel like their blood pressure is going up. Sometimes their heart starts pounding or their breath quickens. It's different for everybody, but try to recognize your own warning signs. If you do, then you can catch yourself and take appropriate action before it's too late.

The main thing to do if you're getting really angry is to stop, take a deep breath, count to ten, and walk away. Do anything to interrupt your natural reaction to fight or attack. We're not talking about actual life threatening events here. We're talking about getting angry when you're at the store, driving, or with family members. Remember that you're trained to react to a real threat by becoming physically aggressive or killing. That reaction can carry over to threats that aren't really life threatening, so you have to learn how to distinguish the difference. Remind yourself that you're not in a war zone anymore. The threats are usually not life or death anymore. Try to adjust your reaction accordingly. I know, it's easier said than done.

Post-Tet Offensive near Saigon, 1968, National Archives

Another issue to discuss with your family is how going to war has changed your perspective on what's really important and what isn't. For example, it might be hard to get all cranked up and sympathetic if your spouse is talking about issues at his or her job like a difficult customer or a hectic schedule. You may find yourself getting irritated by the amount of energy a family member is spending on something that you consider to be trivial in the overall scheme of things. For you, it's not a life or death issue. It's not a big deal compared to the things that you considered to be really important in the war zone. However, to your spouse or children, the everyday issues they deal with are important to them.

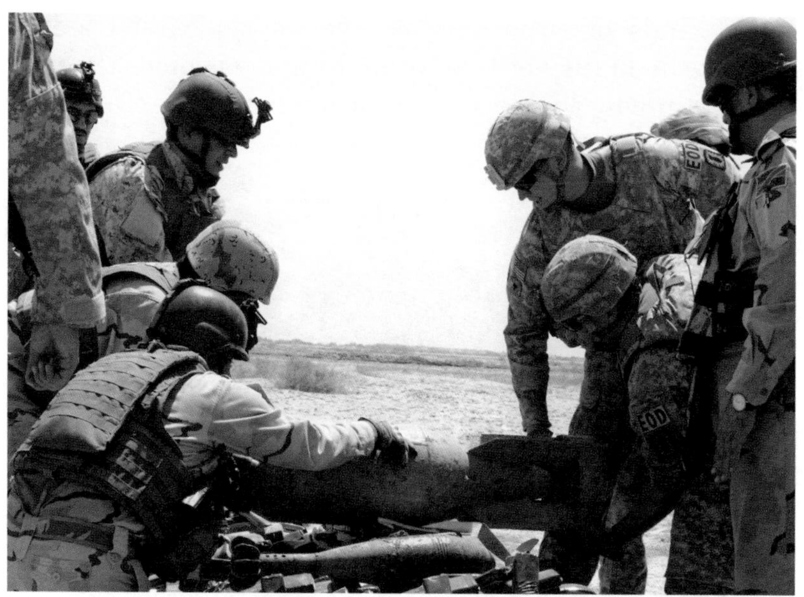

EOD unit with 500 lb. bomb, Iraq, 2010, Dept. of Defense

You may find yourself tuning out when a family member talks about an everyday issue. Family members can often sense that disengagement and detachment. Communicating about it directly is usually the only healthy way of learning to cope with the differences in your values systems. The main thing is to communicate to your family members that you do love and care for them, even if it's hard to express it or show it sometimes. It's important to let them know that you care about their well-being and happiness, even if the day-to-day issues don't feel as important to you. Tell them you want to be there to support them, but maybe they shouldn't always expect you to get as emotionally involved or invested in things after what you've been through. It's important for all of you to try to understand each other's perspectives. The only way to do that is to talk about it openly. As they say, "It's all relative." You may also find yourself getting frustrated at other people's inability to make quick decisions. In combat you have to have the ability to assess a situation immediately and make split second decisions. Try to remember that they haven't been in those kinds of situations, so they're typically used to having the luxury of time in making decisions. Also, try to explain why this is so frustrating for you.

Tigris River patrol boat, Iraq, 2003, Dept. of Defense

What are your other options in terms of anger management? There are many good books and workbooks available with anger management techniques. They can help you identify the thoughts and beliefs you have which affect the way you react in situations. Knowledge is power. The more you know about how your anger works, the better you can manage and control it. Anger management issues can be very costly. They can cost you your family, your job, or your freedom. There are many anger management skills that people can learn to help them live better lives. A good counselor can really help too. Most combat veterans have had many experiences which justifiably result in many underlying layers of anger.

Khe Sahn, Vietnam, 1968, Robert Ellison/Empire News

Khe Sahn, Vietnam, 1968, Paul Stephanus/Empire News

I know you don't want to hear this, but medication is another option. I'm just sayin'. Many believe that after people are exposed to severe stress for extended periods of time, some of their neurotransmitters, or chemicals in the brain, can get depleted. It's like having a car with an engine that is revving at too high a speed that ends up burning through gas and oil faster. Essentially, certain medications can replace those specific neurotransmitters and bring them back up to normal into the average range again. Without those neurotransmitters it can feel like you're trying to run a marathon without enough food or water. Everything feels harder than it should be, or maybe you don't have much energy or motivation to get things done. You might feel tense and "on edge" or irritable all the time. These can be signs that your brain chemistry is out of balance.

I'm not a medical doctor, so I can't give specific advice about which medications to use. I will say that much of the research literature has pointed toward the SSRI class of medications. These are the selective serotonin reuptake inhibitors (SSRI's). Obviously you have to talk to your doctor about this issue, because there are so many other medical factors involved. Only your doctor can make the judgment call about what is the most appropriate medicine for you specifically. It's worth a shot to talk to your doc about it. What have you got to lose? Ideally, it's best to consult with a psychiatrist, since they specialize in treating the subtleties of any condition that has to do with brain chemistry and mood. A psychiatrist has an M.D., whereas a psychologist has a Ph.D. The M.D. can prescribe medications, but the Ph.D. cannot. You can always give it a try and see how it works for you. The SSRIs usually take between 4-6 weeks to take effect, so hang in there and give it a chance to work. In order to get the chemical levels in your brain back up to normal, you have to take the medicine every day, not just when you're feeling badly. If you feel like it's helping for awhile, but then wears off, just tell your doctor. It could be that the dose needs to be adjusted. If you feel like it's not helping you, then tell your doctor, because there are many other medication options available. Why should you feel bad if there's something that can help? If your car runs low on oil, you fill it up. You should consider doing the same thing for your brain if your doctor thinks it will help you.

CHAPTER SEVEN

"I Don't Want To Talk About It"

Most veterans don't like to talk about their bad war experiences, even with their spouses or significant others. It was bad enough to live it. You don't want to have to relive it again by talking about it. It's also painful, and sometimes even traumatic again, to have to dredge it back up. Many people don't tell their spouses about their war experiences, because they don't want them to have the same images in their heads and want to spare them from the truth about what they went

Operation Dewey Canyon, Vietnam, 1969, National Archives

through. They don't need to know the real horrors of war. The thing to remember, though, is that they didn't live the trauma. They're only hearing about it from a safe distance. Of course, they'll be upset to hear about the terrible things that happened to you if they love and care for you. But on the other hand, it frequently pulls couples closer together and will help your spouse understand you better.

Khe Sahn, Vietnam, 1968, Robert Ellison/Empire News

Most veterans don't tell their spouses if they've had a bad nightmare or memory or flashback. They don't want to burden them. However, you need to give them a little more credit. They already know something is bothering you, they just don't know what. As we all know, when things are left up to people's imaginations, they can get blown out of proportion. Most spouses think it's either something that they did or something wrong with the relationship. Or they wonder and worry about what it might be that's upsetting you. Again, in all fairness, it's usually better to tell them you're having a bad day. You don't have to go into specifics. Just say it has to do with the war and leave it at that if you need to. At least that way they won't be worrying and wondering and feel a wedge driven in between the two of you. It's a lot easier for a spouse to have some idea about why you're upset or withdrawn. Then he or she isn't left in the dark to make suppositions and wild guesses. Trust me on this. Most spouses would much rather be "bothered" by you telling them you're having a rough time, than be left in the dark trying to guess. Just ask them, they'll tell you so. They're always telling me that. What have you got to lose by asking?

Marine on night guard against NVA attack, DMZ, Vietnam, 1967, Robert Ellison/Empire News

Most people don't like pain. They will avoid it at all costs. This is another reason people don't want to talk or think about their war experiences. The reason people's traumatic memories are so intense and ever present is because they're spending so much energy trying to push them back into the background somewhere. However, avoiding the memories actually keeps them more alive than recognizing and dealing with them. The classic example of how this works is this: Don't think about a red moose. Whatever you do, push that image out of your mind. For most people the red moose is front and center no matter how hard they try to push it out of their minds. That's how avoiding painful memories works as well. Often the harder you try to avoid them, the more persistent they become. In fact, they frequently push their way into your sleep as nightmares. Those painful memories will be heard one way or another. There's no two ways about it. The only way to get to the other side is through.

WW II, Marine on beach at Eniwetok, 1944, National Archives

WW II Command post in Namur, Belgium, 1944, National Archives

Unfortunately, most people who have been in combat end up thinking about it almost every day anyway. Triggers are everywhere. Sometimes the triggers are obvious, like the news of the current war. Sometimes the triggers are not obvious at all, like hearing somebody's voice who reminds you of a buddy you served with. You can run, but you can't hide. You can try to avoid it, but it's there anyway. If you had a traumatic experience in combat, how could you possibly forget something so powerful, even if you wanted to? People don't want to talk about the trauma or think about it. But it still weasels its way into your thoughts anyway. Somehow you think you're successfully avoiding it as long as you don't actually talk about it. Not true. It's there whether you talk about it or not.

When something is very painful or difficult, we naturally want to avoid anything that reminds us of it, or anything that might trigger the same emotional reaction. That's why some people avoid being with other veterans or might avoid people who physically resemble the enemy. Many war veterans avoid watching movies or things on TV that have to do with war. That's why a person who witnessed a violent bank robbery would probably want to avoid going to the bank, particularly the bank where the robbery actually occurred. Sometimes that person might even end up avoiding the ATM machine, because just the sight of anything to do with the bank can get them upset. In that case we're talking about avoidance of the trigger in order to avoid the arousal or upsetting emotional/physical reaction. I've talked to many war veterans who avoid the beach because the last thing they want to deal with is sand after they've been in the desert. Many guys will avoid going into the woods or hunting if they've been in the jungle. The association between the trigger and the upsetting emotional reactions or memories is so strong that they don't want to subject themselves to it. Actually, if you think about it, that can be a very adaptive coping skill.

Marine cleaning his M-16, Khe Sahn, Vietnam, 1968, Robert Ellison/Empire News

It's only when avoidance interferes with your daily life that it becomes maladaptive. Using the bank example, if the avoidance got to be so strong that the person couldn't even go to the store where they had to pay the cashier, it could cause big problems. That's when the coping mechanism becomes dysfunctional. Avoiding the woods or the beach doesn't really cause that many problems in most people's lives. Even avoiding watching the news or certain movies about war doesn't cause that much interference in our daily lives. If you can make your life less stressful by avoiding the triggers, then by all means do so. No point in making things more difficult for yourself.

Marine in the DMZ, Vietnam, 1967, Robert Ellison/Empire News

I'm not talking about the war veterans who barricade themselves in their houses and don't ever go out. They are usually avoiding being around other people, because they often end up getting angry or don't trust anybody. There has to be some middle ground though. Talking to a counselor can be helpful in trying to find that middle ground. Sometimes you can figure out certain places you might feel comfortable going. I know a guy who used to avoid all public places at all costs. Now, after talking about it, he has come up with the idea of going to a specific restaurant at the time it's the least busy. He knows the employees there and can always sit with his back to the wall where he can see the whole place. This has ended up being a good compromise. It sure has made his wife a whole lot happier! It didn't happen overnight, but it's a good example of how you can better learn to live with some of the things you want to avoid.

Desert Storm oil well fires, 1991, Dept. of Defense

Avoiding talking about or remembering particularly bad events seems like a good idea on the surface. In the short run it can be a good idea because it allows you to carry on with your life and the tasks at hand. However, the emotions and memories associated with it are down there somewhere in your mind, even if you don't talk about them or try not to think about them. That stuff is so powerful that it will be heard one way or another. At some point in the future that stuff will come bubbling up to the surface. So you can do it now, or you can do it later. The way these memories make themselves heard can be through nightmares while you're asleep or through a flashback or a sudden painful memory. The avoidance that you think is helping you can actually be preventing the healing process. Frequently, the healing process involves being able to take the bull by the horns and confronting the painful memories you've been unsuccessfully trying to avoid. Not exactly what you wanted to hear probably.

Desert Storm M-60 machine gunner, 1991, Dept. of Defense

CHAPTER EIGHT

The Lone Ranger

"No man is an island." Unless he's been to war. You'll probably never be as close to another group of people as you were with your battle buddies. You trusted them with your life, and they trusted you with theirs. You were willing to lay down your life for them, and they for you, if that's what it took. There's even a quote in the Bible about that. "Greater love hath no man than this, that a man lay down his life for his friends" (John 15:13).

Fallen soldier, Afghanistan, 2004, Dept. of Defense

If you've been to war you've seen the best in people and the worst in people. You've seen the evil that humans can inflict on one another. You may have even inflicted bad things on people yourself. Either way, you know what people are fully capable of, particularly in desperate situations. That's one of the reasons it's so hard for you to trust anybody. I mean *really* trust other people. If you're lucky you trust your spouse or certain members of your family. But once your innocence is lost, there's no going back. You have learned in life or death situations that you can't take a chance on people who don't deserve your trust. You've learned that trust and respect are things that have to be earned. You've seen people who tried to command it, even when they didn't deserve it. You've probably seen orders handed down that you knew damn well might needlessly cost people's lives, maybe even your own.

Samarra, Iraq, 2004, Dept. of Defense

You might have seen the totally unnecessary loss of life due to somebody's stubbornness as a result of their rank. They figured they knew better than you guys since they were higher up in the chain of command. Tell me that doesn't make you angry. So again, I say your trust and respect are things which have to be earned. As a result of that, you probably have only a handful of people or less whom you would consider a true friend. Somebody you could call at 3 a.m. and know they'd really be there for you in a heartbeat, no questions asked. Civilian life doesn't lend itself to a whole lot of opportunities to test somebody's character in ways that it really counts. The good news is that as a result of your experiences, you're probably fairly good at reading other people. It's always good to trust your instincts. It's kept you alive thus far, so it must be pretty spot on.

Stryker Brigade, Afghanistan, 2010, Dept. of Defense

Many war veterans choose to avoid people because they feel it's just a big source of irritation. People who have no military experience don't have the level of training and awareness that was drilled into you. It started in boot camp. "Stay alert, stay alive." How many times have you heard that? This is why you find it incredibly aggravating when somebody isn't paying attention in traffic and cuts you off or makes some other potentially dangerous mistake. You think to yourself, "Nobody can be that stupid! They must be doing that on purpose." Well, guess again. Most people are just paying attention to the car ahead of them. Maybe they're talking on their cell phone. They don't realize that death is a reality. You know it's a reality. You know how fragile life is. To most people death in accidents is only a concept, idea, or abstract thing. Maybe they've seen it in movies, television or books. But that does not make it a reality for them, so they don't necessarily think something like that is really possible.

Medics in Afghanistan, 2010, Dept. of Defense

Naturally, it makes you very angry when you see somebody being so careless. This is what contributes to road rage, and I do mean rage. It's a natural reaction as a result of your experiences. Try to remember that most people don't have your level of awareness, preparedness and training. They probably aren't doing it on purpose most of the time, so try, if you can, to take a deep breath. In the long run it's not worth it to get that cranked up about it. Allowing yourself to become enraged will only ruin your day, not theirs. And it certainly won't change who and what they are. Do yourself a favor and try to let it roll by.

When you know how angry you can get in situations like that you tend to avoid people. It takes a lot of energy to control your temper. If you know how enraged you can become and what you're capable of, you tend to avoid situations that might provoke your anger. That's probably a good idea for the most part. If it is interfering with your ability to live your life and conduct your daily affairs, then avoidance can become a problem. It's okay if you don't want to socialize a lot. It can be hard on your spouse though. Family members usually haven't been through the experiences you have, so they still probably enjoy being around other people.

Vietnam, 1967, Paul Stephanus/Empire News

Communication and compromise are the keys here. Explain to your spouse why you don't like being around people. If he or she understands why, it might make it a little easier to deal with. Try to come up with ideas of things you can do together that don't involve a lot of people. Try to pick a few people you can tolerate being around and get together with them. Have an agreement beforehand that you'll let him or her know when you've had enough and are ready to leave. You may not like going

Combat Control Team, Iraq, 2003, Dept. of Defense

to crowded restaurants, even if you can sit where you can see the door and all the people. Come up with a compromise like going to a restaurant at the least crowded time. Pick one where you are familiar with some of the people who work there. Again, decide beforehand that if you get too antsy you'll be able to leave. The main thing is that you don't feel trapped in a very uncomfortable situation. Again, explain to your spouse that staying aware of all your surroundings was one of the ways that helped you stay alive. You had to be aware of who was where and any potential threats there might be. Many times this was a 24 hour a day, 7 day a week necessity. Old habits, particularly those involving life or death, don't die easily.

If you don't trust people and have had bad experiences with those higher up in your chain of command, then you probably have what they call "difficulties with authority." Respect and leadership have to be earned, particularly on the battlefield. Sometimes warriors are forced into situations where they have to obey orders from somebody who may not be directly involved in the situation or may not have as much experience or information. However they have the ability to hand down orders by virtue of their rank. As I mentioned before, if you've seen those in positions of authority abuse and use their

Samarra, Iraq, 2004, Dept. of Defense

power in less than admirable ways, you're less likely to take a position of authority at face value. You may have a really bad taste in your mouth for authority figures.

Several times I've heard about new superiors ordering the unit into formation in a dangerous area. The more experienced guys said it was a bad idea because it could get people killed. The new "know-it-all" thought he knew better because he had a higher rank. Well, you probably know the rest. Sometimes the obvious attack occurred and people died, for no damn reason other than stupidity. Or maybe there was the inevitable attack, but luckily, nobody died or was wounded, including you. In your mind you've associated authority figures with bullies or idiots as a result of some bad experiences you may have had. Obviously, there is a lot of fantastic leadership in all branches of the military. But it only takes one bad seed to leave that bad taste in your mouth, particularly in a war zone, where the stakes are so high. If you can, try not to make the assumption that all those in authority are bullies or idiots. Try to withhold judgment until you see for yourself.

Waiting in an alley, Fallujah, Iraq, 2004, Dept. of Defense

"I don't want to get close to anybody." Emotional detachment is a coping strategy people develop to avoid pain. It's very effective in a war zone. If you get too attached to somebody, there's a chance they might be gone in a heartbeat. The most logical way to deal with that is to turn off your emotions. That's basically what emotional detachment is. It's an effective coping skill in a war zone, but not so much with your spouse, kids, significant other, family and friends. They want the "old" you back. They still want the emotional connection you used to have. Once again, compromise can be a good thing. Counselors can help with this, too. It doesn't have to be all or nothing. You can learn ways to get closer to the people you love without laying yourself wide open to emotional devastation. It's not an overnight thing, but it's certainly worth trying if it means saving your relationships.

River patrol boat, Vietnam, 1967, National Archives

CHAPTER NINE

You Can Run But You Can't Hide

Many people ask why a memory from so many years ago can be so crystal clear. There's a good explanation for that. The mind is biologically set up in such a way that one of the emotion centers (the amygdala) is located right next to one of the long-term memory storage centers (the hippocampus). The reason humans are wired that way is so that an event with intense emotion will be burned into their memory banks. For example, take the saber tooth tiger attack. If you want to survive the next time, you better remember what it looks like, what it sounds like, what it smells like, where it lives, etc.

Desert Storm, 1991, Dept. of Defense

The fear you experience during the attack burns that information into your memory banks. That way you will hopefully be able to avoid the attack by the tiger in the future. It serves an important function in survival. Your intense fear causes you to store that vital information, so you won't have to go through the life-threatening experience again. This explains why you can't remember what you had for breakfast last week (no emotions attached to it), but you can remember a firefight from a long time ago with distinct clarity as if it was yesterday.

The good news is that this biological arrangement of our brains helps us survive as a species. The bad news is that most terrifying, horrifying, enraging, grief-stricken, or even intensely joyous, events are burned into our brains forever. It might be an intensely happy event like the birth of your child or your graduation. However, for most people who have been to war, the terrifying, horrific, horrible scenes are some of the images burned into their minds. That is why it's so hard to forget particu-

WW II Bougainville, 1944, National Archives

larly traumatic events. In war they're usually life-threatening, so they really grab hold. Your brain doesn't want you to be in those situations again, so it keeps reminding you about the dangers and details associated with them. So when people tell you "that was in the past, so just get over it," you might want to educate them about this. If they've been through something horrific or terrifying themselves, they won't be able to forget that either. Usually they're lucky enough never to have experienced anything as traumatic as combat.

Khe Sahn, Vietnam, 1968, Robert Ellison/Empire News

Many people will describe their memory of a traumatic event as "snapshots" of the event, as opposed to more like a running tape. That's because usually, there's so much information coming in all at once that it's impossible to process it all. This is particularly true if the person is in a state of heightened emotional arousal. If you're in a firefight, you're being bombarded with sights, sounds, smells, sensations and critical information all at once. It's impossible to experience each part of that, so the less important parts don't quite make it into the memory banks. You're more likely to remember the parts which were critical to your survival at the time. The rest gets filtered out by the brain as less important. After all, if your life is on the line, your brain isn't going to waste precious energy and attention on anything that isn't of the utmost importance. That's why you are left with a bunch of snapshots. A person's sensations, perceptions and sense of time usually get distorted when they're under extreme stress as well.

Khe Sahn, Vietnam, 1968, Robert Ellison/Empire News

WW I, France, National Archives

Sometimes people totally block out or "forget" particularly difficult or traumatic events altogether. It's our mind's way of protecting us. It's sort of like when an engine overheats. It shuts down. Another example is when a hard drive on a computer gets its memory overloaded and then crashes and turns off. The mind is like that too when it's experiencing information overload, or emotion overload. When there have already been so many traumatic events in the recent past, sometimes the mind just can't handle even one more bad thing. So a person can be physically there and acting almost on "auto pilot" but have no memory of the event. Their mind has had enough and doesn't want any more to deal with. I don't know how many times I've heard people say there are pieces of time missing from a traumatic event. They may say the explosion occurred and the next thing they remember is being back at the FOB (forward operating base) with blood on their clothes, even though they were conscious the whole time. The actual event is blocked from their memory. I know a machine gunner who was in Vietnam who can't remember ever firing his weapon. He could remember carrying it, and the guys told him he was really good at using it. However, he has no actual memory of having fired it. That's called dissociation. It can be as if the mind has pulled the plug on the really bad stuff to protect itself.

Civil War, National Archives

Warriors will sometimes describe dissociation as "the day I forgot" or "after the explosion, the next thing I remember is being back on the FOB." Then, sometimes out of nowhere, a memory will come back, like a mission which had been forgotten or not thought about since coming home. Usually, something in the present triggers the memory. You might be shocked that you could've forgotten something so significant. There's usually a good reason you didn't remember it. Typically, it might have very intense, unpleasant emotions associated with it, so your mind protects you from it. Or sometimes there are so many bad days and missions that they all kind of blur together. Only the most horrific or dangerous ones stand out. The rest may pale by comparison so they get lost in the shuffle until something in the present brings them to the forefront. One guy said he was watching television when he saw a mountain range he'd been on during a covert mission. Wham! Out of nowhere the memory came at him full force. It can be very disconcerting, but be assured that it is part of the unloading or healing process. The memories are there, sometimes lurking in the background. They need to come out at some point for the healing to take place.

Spent shell casings, Khe Shan, Vietnam,1968, Robert Ellison/Empire News

It's hard to really process or fully debrief from a traumatic incident with just a bunch of random pieces of memory or snapshots. That's why it's important to be able to talk about the event in detail. I know that's not what you want to hear, but it's the truth. The only way to get to the other side is to go through. This is best done with a trained therapist or counselor. Nobody wants to go back and recreate the scene, because it's too painful and horrific. However, it is critically important to be able to fill in the blanks between those snapshots. There is always very valuable information that needs to be discovered to complete the picture. One of the main reasons the memories continue to haunt people is because they're not complete or finished. You've heard the expression "unfinished business." This is a good example of that. You can't really put it away until you've filled in the blanks and finished the business of debriefing.

WW II Jungle Raiders, 1944, National Archives

There are certain kinds of treatments that help people recreate the stressful event in order to make sense of both the facts and the emotions. One of these treatments is called Prolonged Exposure Therapy. This involves describing the traumatic event over and over again until it loses some of its emotional power. At first glance, people usually think, "No way am I going to go back over that horrible event over and over again!" Just know that whether you talk about it and remember it

Fallujah, Iraq, 2004, Dept. of Defense

overtly or not, it's still floating around in there below the surface. That biological link I talked about between the emotion center and the memory center will make sure it's burned into your memory banks, so it's better to take the bull by the horns and talk about it. Talking about a bad memory never killed anybody. If you're doing it with a trained therapist, then they're not going to let you decompensate and you won't "go crazy." Most people are afraid they might open the flood gates of emotion and never be able to stop. That's also not true. Getting the emotions up and out can actually be a big relief. Blowing off that steam that's bottled up inside is imperative to the healing process.

Another treatment is called Cognitive Processing Therapy. This involves examining the effects of the traumatic event on your beliefs, values, and attitudes. The experiences in combat have deep and lasting effects on how people live the rest of their lives. It affects your beliefs about yourself and the world. You then adjust your behaviors and values accordingly. For example, your ability to trust others and be emotionally close to them is definitely affected. Cognitive Processing Therapy explores issues like safety, trust, intimacy and the meaning of the traumatic event. All of these areas are explored in this type of treatment so that you can be aware of which beliefs and attitudes are working for you and which are not. Then you can adapt and modify your reactions in ways that work best for you.

A moment of prayer before a mission, Iraq, 2009, Dept. of Defense

Surprisingly, people often end up remembering very important pieces of the traumatic event that hadn't been originally encoded. As I mentioned before, information overload can occur when there are so many sights, sounds, smells and sensations coming at you so quickly while your adrenalin is in overdrive during combat. After the traumatic event is over, your brain has encoded the somewhat filtered information, not all the actual facts. For example, a warrior might have frozen up and didn't pull the trigger fast enough. As a result of that, he experienced tremendous guilt, feeling he must have frozen out of fear or cowardice. When reviewing the facts of the event, he recalled that there had been an explosion at the same time, which had temporarily distracted him. This definitely changed how he viewed his behavior and had been incorrectly blaming himself for being scared and screwing up. This is a good reason to fill in the gaps in the memories of an event, particularly if you have guilt or regret about the situation.

Hue City Citadel, Vietnam, Tet Offensive, 1968, Paul Stephanus/Empire News

Many Vietnam War, Korean War or WWII veterans have successfully blocked out their painful memories for decades. Maybe they've had nightmares, but they were able to keep themselves distracted and busy with work and raising their families. This allowed them to avoid the memories for a long time. But once the distractions and pressures of work are gone, the void that's left behind makes way for the past to come to the surface. I've lost count of the number of people who said they couldn't believe that these memories were coming back as clearly as if it were yesterday, even though it's been 30 or 40 years since they were on the battlefield. You can run, but you can't hide.

Hue City, Vietnam, Tet Offensive, 1968, Paul Stephanus/Empire News

In fact, the human brain is anatomically configured so that any experience that has very intense emotion associated with it gets burned into our memory banks. The brain is hardwired that way. The amygdala (emotion center) is associated with intense, primitive emotions, like rage, terror, fear and horror. The hippocampus is partly responsible for long-term memory storage. Those two brain structures are located right next to each other, which is one of the reasons an emotionally intense experience gets deeply encoded into the memory. Many think that this anatomical arrangement is tied to the survival instincts. If you're being chased by a saber tooth tiger, you better remember what it looks like, sounds like, smells like, etc., if you want to avoid being attacked by him in the future and survive. Like I said, this results in traumatic experiences with intense, primitive emotions being burned into the memory banks.

Khe Sahn, Vietnam, 1968, Robert Ellison/Empire News

Chapter Ten

Comfortably Numb

As I said, nobody likes pain. Combat usually involves pain, discomfort, and generally unpleasant emotions and sensations. Naturally, once it's over, people want to forget about it and get on with their lives. This makes sense. Many people figure that a quick, easy fix for that is alcohol or drugs. Mind-altering substances have a way of making people forget their pain, at least temporarily anyway. They can numb the pain and provide some relief. That's why so many people "self-medicate" their pain after combat. It seems like the appropriate thing to do at the time, particularly since it seems to work in the short run. However, you can't drown the memories into nonexistence. You might get a temporary respite from the painful memories, but they're still there after the buzz wears off.

DMZ, Vietnam, 1967, Robert Ellison/Empire News

Remember, there's a biological reason why the bad memories remain, hard as we try to get rid of them. Alcohol might temporarily help you "forget" the painful memories, but they're always still there once you sober up. The truth is, there's not enough alcohol or drugs in the whole world to drown those memories or erase those experiences.

Many combat veterans I've talked with drank pretty heavily after first returning home from the war zone. Some drank to forget the bad memories and some drank to calm their nerves. There's a certain degree of high tension and "high alert status" that stays turned on after coming home. It's like a car running at a high idle speed. It's not so easy to turn it back down to regular idle

WW II, Rangers, National Archive

speed once you're home. It's not like a light switch, which can be flipped off. That high alert status kept you alive in the war zone and in combat. It's become a survival instinct now. It's a double-edged sword. It keeps you and your family safe, but it makes it pretty hard for you to relax. This is another reason so many people drink after returning home from war. "I just want to relax a little bit and take the edge off." Again, alcohol or drugs might work temporarily, but not in the long run.

WW II, Cape Gloucester, 1944, National Archives

Alcohol overuse or drug abuse usually cause big problems at home and at work. No moral judgment there, just the reality of the situation. So what's a person to do instead? It's a good idea to start by looking at what other stress management techniques have worked for you in the past. Exercise is usually a great way to burn off some of your tension and stress. It also makes you feel like you're accomplishing something and taking control of the situation. Sitting at home or at the bar drinking, not so much. Taking the bull by the horns and forcing yourself to exercise is much more proactive and makes you feel better about yourself. You know how it is. At first it's pretty hard to get motivated, but then the benefits kick in and you really do start to feel less stressed. Obviously, the likelihood of succeeding with exercise is increased if you have a workout buddy or make yourself accountable to somebody else. Routine and structure also help you keep with the program, even when your motivation and enthusiasm are waning. It's also good to make sure you're eating right and drinking enough water. Caffeine is a stimulant. If you're already wound pretty tight, cut back on the caffeine. It can make a difference.

Relaxation exercises are a way of teaching your body to override the stress response. It's been scientifically proven that people can learn to control their heart rates, muscle tension, breathing, body's stress reaction, pain levels and even blood pressure. Biofeedback is a fancy way of measuring these things with machines and telling you how well you're doing at controlling them. However, people can learn to control their muscle tension, stress levels and breathing by using very simple techniques. Deep breathing techniques involve taking slow, deep breaths. Ideally, you should get into a comfortable position in a quiet environment if possible. If not, you can practice this anywhere. Take a slow, deep breath in and hold it for a count of three to five seconds. Then slowly release it while you count the seconds again. Keep repeating this until you're able to get your breathing rate slowed down. This technique accomplishes a couple of goals. It helps you focus on your own body and breathing rather than on the thoughts that are making you tense or upset. Secondly, it increases the oxygen flow to your brain and body, preventing hyperventilation and increased feelings of anxiety. The more you practice this technique, the easier it becomes and the more effective it is.

Another relaxation technique involves muscle relaxation. Try tensing up your shoulders before you try to relax them. That's a lot easier than just trying to relax your shoulders first. Being able to feel the extreme tension in your muscle group first allows you to achieve a deeper level of relaxation, by contrast. It's sort of like pulling a pendulum to the right. It will swing farther to the left as a result of the momentum, than if you had started in the middle. The same thing goes for your muscle groups. So, start at the top of your head or the bottom of your feet and begin first tensing and then relaxing each muscle group. Tense the muscle group and hold it for three to five seconds. Then let go and let it relax for several seconds. Try this three or four times with each muscle group. This works like the deep breathing technique from the standpoint of drawing your focus away from your worries and stress and onto your body.

If the deep breathing or muscle relaxation techniques don't appeal to you, try the imagery technique. This involves imagining yourself in a peaceful, relaxed, calm, tranquil environment. Yes, this is "going to your happy place." Again, try to get into a comfortable position in a quiet environment, if possible. Think of the place where you feel most at peace. Maybe it's the beach or the mountains or a hammock. Imagine yourself in that place and try to pay attention to your five senses. Try to imagine how the temperature or sun or breeze feels on your skin. Try to imagine the sounds and sights there. If there are any tastes associated with the location, then try to imagine that as well. Try to pay attention to the aspects of your peaceful place that help you feel relaxed. The more you practice this exercise, the better you'll get at being able to go straight to a very relaxed feeling just by thinking about the place.

Another avenue to explore is medication. I know, nobody likes taking pills. I'm not a pill-pusher. I can't even prescribe medication, since I don't have an M.D. degree. However, as I said before, being under extended periods of stress can deplete some of the neurotransmitters in your brain. There are certain medications, SSRI antidepressants, which have been very successful in bringing those brain chemicals back up to the normal levels where they should be. It doesn't necessarily have to be a lifetime commitment. It is worth a try though, if your doctor thinks it's appropriate for you. Most of the people I know who've tried medication have said it really helped to "take the edge off." I'm not talking about addictive medications here that alter your state of consciousness or awareness. These aren't "uppers" or "downers." These are just medications that replace the chemicals that have been depleted. If you had diabetes, you'd take insulin to replace what's gone. This isn't much different, in the sense that you're replacing the necessary chemicals that have been depleted. If you think this might be an option for you, speak to your physician or mental health professional. Only your licensed medical provider can determine which, if any, medications are appropriate for you.

Hai Van Pass, Vietnam, 1968, Paul Stephanus/Empire News

CHAPTER ELEVEN

Cold As Ice

Most veterans of war are described as being "cold, unemotional, hard" or have been told "you just don't seem to care." You would probably describe yourself as emotionally detached or unemotional as well. Many veterans describe themselves as emotionally numb and don't even cry at family members' funerals. Naturally, this disturbs some of you when you can't even cry at your own loved one's funeral, for example. You think that you should feel something or be sad or show some kind of emotion. Somehow, though, it's just not there. There seems to be a void where the sadness should be. But just try listening to "Taps" without getting choked up, or think about how you felt when your last pet died. You can't tell me that's not very intense emotion. It's just selective, not absent.

Sniper in Afghanistan, 2004, Dept. of Defense

In my experience, many war veterans actually have very deep emotions. They're not easily accessed or expressed, but that doesn't mean the emotions aren't there. I like to use the term "selective emotion." You've heard of selective memory, where you remember the things you really want to, but forget the things you don't want to remember. Like "forgetting" to take out the garbage. It's also kind of like "selective hearing." I'm sure you've tuned out your spouse or some other relative on more than one occasion. Maybe you were tired of listening to the same old thing or felt like you were being nagged. We've all been there. The way we cope is by tuning out the things that are unpleasant or painful or useless.

Amputation, Civil War, National Archives

In a war zone, emotion is not appropriate. It can cost people their lives if they get emotional in a crisis situation. If you get emotional in combat, your senses won't be as sharp as they need to be to survive. Stay alert, stay alive. Focus on the mission. Suck it up and push forward. That is the way it has to be in combat if you want to stay alive. It's absolutely essential and extremely adaptive to learn how to be able to totally shut down your emotions. Considering that the stakes are life and death, you get really good at it really quickly. Just like many of the other response systems, the shutting down of the normal "emotional response system" is not like the light switch that can be flipped back on once you're home from war.

Fallujah, Iraq, 2004, Dept. of Defense

As you can imagine, having an "emotional response system" that is locked down good and tight doesn't usually sit well with spouses or family members who are waiting for you back home. They've typically got their emotional response systems still up and running, possibly even on overdrive, since they're so emotional about you coming home alive. They may have had to turn down their emotional attachment while you've been gone to protect themselves. That's adaptive too. Sometimes when both people are emotionally detached it's hard to cross the distance.

Afghanistan, 2010, Dept. of Defense

Military culture. Being in the service teaches you a lot of self-discipline, work ethic, responsibility, leadership skills, courage, and how to handle just about any emergency that arises. However, some of the values and traditions which are critical for functioning well in the military don't always transfer well to civilian life afterwards. It is critical in combat to be able to disengage completely from one's emotions. If you don't, it's likely to get you killed. I heard somebody say one time, "Just because somebody gets killed or something blows up, doesn't mean your day is over." You absolutely have to "suck it up and move on." No ifs, ands or buts. That ability to turn off your emotions serves you well in that environment, but not so much once you get home.

Once you're back at home, your family members are not expecting you to behave like you had to in the war zone. They're expecting you to be able to reconnect with them emotionally. When that doesn't seem to be occurring, they can get upset and hurt. They can frequently take that personally, as if you don't love them or care for them like you used to. If they're feeling that way, they may withdraw or try to push you into reconnecting. Sometimes this can result in arguments and cause even more stress. It's important for both you and your family members to understand where this emotional detachment and "sucking it up" came from. It's a self-protective coping skill that most people develop out of necessity. It's going to take time, readjustment and the rebuilding of relationships for your emotional responsiveness to develop again. It's going to require shifting some gears from being so stoic to trying to be more authentic and forthcoming with the effects of the traumatic experiences. Communication is the key here.

Hue City, Vietnam, Tet Offensive, 1968, Paul Stephanus/Empire News

Try to talk about it with your spouse. Do your best to explain it, or let them read this book. At least then they'll know it's not just you, or not just them. This is what most people go through, particularly initially after returning from deployment.

Khe Sahn, Vietnam, 1968, Robert Ellison/Empire News

When you've lost a buddy in combat, the pain can be overwhelming. Nobody likes pain. Especially not that kind of pain. It's like when the body goes into shock after it's been wounded. The mind can go into shock as well. In Vietnam, the expression was "it don't mean a thing" or "it don't mean nothin'." At times like that, when you've lost a friend but have to press forward and keep on going, it seems like just the right thing to say. It's the best way to cope at the time. However, the death of a friend deserves to be honored and mourned and respected. It can't be shut away and ignored forever. Eventually, the grief, anger and sadness have to come out. Besides, you owe it to his or her memory to acknowledge what they meant to you. Some guys I know will have their own memorial for somebody they lost. Maybe the date he or she was killed is marked by having a toast of his favorite drink. Maybe it's listening to her favorite song. Maybe it's having a moment of silence. Maybe it's looking at the old pictures you brought home. The point is, you both deserve to recognize and commemorate their life or lives. It's the right thing to do. Crying is okay too. Whoever said "real men don't cry" hadn't met many men who have been to war. Most of the men and women I've met who have experienced the tragedies of war have shed a tear at one point or another. There is no shame in expressing emotion for somebody who was there to watch your back and would've given up his or her life for yours if needed.

Memorial service, Iraq, 2007, Dept. of Defense

Warriors are trained not to cry or show emotion. But if you have a soul, there is no shame in grieving and crying for somebody whose life was taken in war. Sadness and emotional pain are natural human emotions, and crying is the way human beings are wired to express it. I can tell you that almost all of the combat veterans I've spoken to have cried or teared up at least once. If you've lost a brother or a sister in combat or witnessed the tragedies and horrific, traumatic events of war, then you've earned the right to cry. If you don't cry about those unspeakable things, then when would it ever be appropriate? As I said, if you have a soul, then you'll probably cry, or at least wish you could.

Memorial in Iraq, 2009, Dept. of Defense

It's a healthy thing to get the tears and sadness out. It's like lancing a boil to get the bad stuff out. It's cathartic and necessary. Even if you feel emotionally numb most of the time, I'll bet there are certain memories that can make you cry. Hearing "Taps" or "Amazing Grace" on the bagpipes cuts right through all the societal expectations. It goes right to the heart and soul of the emotions that we all feel at some time or another. Don't buy into the phony expectations that warriors don't cry. That's a crock. Combat warriors are the ones who have the most reasons to cry. You've lived through hell. You, above most others, have earned the right. So make use of the right you've earned and allow your sadness and tears to flow. It's part of the healing process. I guarantee you that any other combat veteran who sees you cry or tear up has felt the same way. I've seen it too many times in the combat veterans' groups. If one of the guys gets choked up, everybody is right there telling him it's okay. They say that because they, of all people know it's natural and appropriate. There is no shame in a warrior's tears. It's a testimony and proof of what he or she has been through. It's the memorial to those whose lives have been lost. There is no shame there, only honor.

Memorial service in Iraq, 2009, Dept. of Defense

Chapter Twelve

The Pucker Factor

Fear. Anybody who's been to war and tells you they weren't afraid is probably just trying to act tough. I read someplace that the definition of bravery or courage is being afraid but doing it anyway. Fear is a natural instinct that all animals have, particularly human beings with our higher level of consciousness. It's a survival skill. Physical pain is the body's way of letting you know something is wrong. Fear is the mind's way of letting you know something is wrong. It's part of the "fight, flight or freeze" reaction that most people have in response to a dangerous threat. It's the body's way of gearing up either to fight for it's life or run like hell to

Recon in Iraq, 2003, Dept. of Defense

escape the danger. The body kicks into overdrive with stress hormones firing on all cylinders, muscles tensing up for action, and even blood flow being diverted to the extremities. The heart rate typically speeds up, and the adrenalin kicks in. You know the feeling I'm talking about. The adrenalin rush can even become addictive for some people. They get to the point where they miss the high it can give them. Sometimes this contributes to thrill seeking behaviors after they get home from the war zone, such as taking the motorcycle over 100 mph, getting into fights, and other adrenalin pumping activities. Remember the movie line "I feel the need, the need for speed." That pretty much sums it up.

WW II, Iwo Jima, 1945, National Archives

Sometimes fear is so overwhelming that it causes people to freeze up. They can't decide whether to fight or flee. Maybe there's too much information coming at them from too many different directions all at once.

Maybe they're still trying to decide how to react. Since it's a life or death situation, it's probably better not to make the wrong choice between fight or flight (flee). It takes a lightning fast assessment of the situation. And don't forget, people's sensory systems are typically overwhelmed by all the sights, sounds, smells, etc. Time

WW II, Peleliu Island, 1944, National Archives

and sensory information can get distorted. Then throw in the fear and anger, which are in over-drive because of the adrenalin. This makes for a pretty difficult situation under severe duress. Survival is a very strong driving force for all living things. Frequently, taking action in a combat situation involves your mind willingly overriding what your genetics have programmed into you. For example, running toward a situation that you know might kill you. That requires your brain to override your survival instinct. Often the training takes over automatically in situations like that. This is why the military has people train and train and train again. It has to become automatic, almost reflex, so that it takes precedent over rational thinking. Let's face it. Rational thinking would tell most people to run away from the people who are trying to kill them in most civilian circumstances. However, combat ain't normal circumstances. Quite the contrary.

The more recently developed higher part of the human brain, the cortex, is responsible for making the rational decisions. It is responsible for scheduling appointments, paying bills, making everyday decisions and the like. That's all fine in regular life circumstances.

Iraq, 2003, Dept. of Defense

However, the deeper, older parts of the human brain, like the amygdala and limbic system, are more primitive. They react in more of an animal fashion than the logical, more sophisticated parts of the brain. They don't engage in cost/benefit analyses or weigh the consequences in a situation. It's pure animal, emotional reaction. If the predominant emotion is anger or rage, then the reaction is likely to be to want to attack and become aggressive. If the prominent emotion is fear or horror, the natural reaction is to get away as fast as possible. Nobody likes pain, especially not the primitive parts of our brain. As far as those parts of the brain are concerned pleasure=good, pain=bad. You'll notice there is no rational thought in either of those two equations. It's sort of the auto-pilot part of the brain, if you will. It takes the more sophisticated rational thinking mind to act as the active, real pilot in any situation. This is where more sophisticated concepts like loyalty, duty, honor, courage and doing your job come in.

There you are about to engage in combat. All parts of the brain are reacting, along with all the physical reactions taking place. It can be an overwhelming and surreal feeling. Hopefully, the training and active pilot will take over and respond accordingly. However, sometimes the auto-pilot kicks in or the system gets so overloaded that it feels like it shuts down temporarily. This is the "freeze" reaction people can have. It just

Afghanistan, 2010, Dept. of Defense

happens sometimes. It's nature taking over. It's nothing to feel ashamed of or embarrassed about. It's a matter of survival. Nobody knows how they're going to react in a life or death situation until they're actually in one. You can prepare and prepare to the best of your ability. But when it really happens and you're in the thick of things with real bullets, sometimes the auto-pilot just takes over. This is why people should try not to feel guilty if they've ever frozen up in a combat situation. Easier said than done. I'm just sayin'. There are real, physiological, hardwired reasons for this kind of response. Before you judge yourself or somebody else too harshly, just take those factors into consideration. Biology is sometimes stronger than rational thought. Just ask any teenage boy when his hormones are raging. I rest my case.

CHAPTER THIRTEEN

"I've Been Depressed For No Reason Lately"

Emotions are not random. They don't just spring up out of nowhere for no reason. If you're experiencing an emotion there's always a valid reason for it. You may not be able to figure it out at first glance, but that doesn't mean there isn't a good reason behind it. Maybe you've been more irritable or depressed lately "for no reason." I was talking to a guy recently who said that things were going pretty well in his life so he didn't know why he was feeling down in the dumps. A good place to start is to think back to what was happening while you were in the war zone during this time of the year. It might

Beirut, USS Cole bombing, 2000, Dept. of Defense

be an anniversary reaction. Maybe it's the actual month, or maybe it's before the month of the trauma. Sometimes people can anticipate the anniversary ahead of time and start to experience those emotions but don't realize it.

Most people have some sort of "internal time clock." That internal awareness may be experiencing something unconsciously that we may not be aware of in our conscious mind. Many times this can be an "anniversary reaction." Just like people have regular anniversaries for happy things like weddings, they also have anniversary reactions for sad things like the death of a loved one or other traumas. An anniversary reaction can occur for you if you've had something terrible happen, like buddies being killed or getting wounded yourself. It might be a tragic accident that occurred or a particularly horrific firefight. It can be almost anything that was horrific or traumatic. For some people it's when they arrived at or left the war zone. Any time of great significance to you can result in an anniversary reaction.

WW II, Omaha Beach, 1944, National Archives

Usually, people in combat aren't paying attention to a calendar, unless they're short-timers. This was particularly true back before I-pods, computers and other forms of modern technology. Back then you were lucky if you knew what month it was. When something traumatic happens, it can leave something like a "muscle memory" of sorts. Even if you're not paying attention consciously to the date on the calendar, your body remembers and recognizes the time of the year anyway. It's something more primitive than conscious awareness and logic. Sometimes people who are feeling particularly tense or depressed "for no reason" can be experiencing some kind of anniversary reaction and don't even realize it.

Memorial service, Iraq, 2003, Dept. of Defense

One of the important things about anniversaries is that they need to be honored. Usually, in combat, you don't have the luxury of an official memorial service. And if you do, it's short and sweet. I heard somebody say they weren't even finished with a memorial service when a firefight erupted just outside the FOB (forward operating base), so it had to be cut short. I'm talking again about unfinished business. Unresolved grief is a big part of anniversary reactions. That's why it's important to be aware of it, so you can honor and pay respect to the person or people involved, even if it was you yourself who was wounded or traumatized. I recall that a cable channel had a show depicting war veterans talking about celebrating their "alive day." They were referring to the day on which they almost died but didn't. So it became their "alive day." That is certainly an important anniversary with a lot of emotion tied to it.

Loading wounded, Iraq, 2004, Dept. of Defense

In all societies there are rituals to honor or commemorate a person's death. In war, people are frequently robbed of that ritual. Sometimes they didn't even know if a person lived or died. All they knew was that they put them on a chopper and that was it. Try to come up with your own way of paying your respects to a life that was taken. Have five minutes of silence. Write the person a letter and then burn or bury it. Have a toast of his or her favorite drink in that person's memory. Look at photos. Whatever makes you feel you have taken time out to pay your respects. It's probably going to be painful, but it needs to be done. One guy I know tries to go to the base here in the States where they have headstones honoring the members of their unit who were killed in action. He tries to go there every year on the anniversary of his friends' deaths. Yes, it's sad and very emotional, but it's also healing. Memorial Day is another time to pay respects to your own people in particular. Memorial Day and July 4th, or other patriotic holidays, can be like anniversaries or painful reminders of the cost of freedom.

Iraq, 2003, Dept. of Defense

When depression begins to take over and stays with you all the time, it can be overwhelming. People can feel trapped and begin to feel hopeless. Hopelessness can cause people to give up and feel like there is no purpose to their lives anymore. Sometimes the depression can become so emotionally painful that people become desperate. This is when people sometimes begin to think about suicide. Most people don't really want to end their lives, but they can feel like there is no other way to end their emotional pain. If you're having suicidal thoughts now, please call 1-800-273-8255 or 911 right away. The 1-800 number is the Suicide Prevention Hotline, and there are people there who talk specifically with veterans. Don't worry that they're going to have you locked up. The people on the other end of the telephone line are there to talk to you without judgment. They are there because they understand some of what you're going through and want to help you get through the worst of it.

Korea, 1950, National Archives

Sometime in war there are so many traumatic events in succession that they can get blurred together. In cases like that, you may only really think about an anniversary reaction in association with the most significant traumatic events. However, if you're feeling depressed "for no reason," again try to think back on what was happening around that time period when you were in the war zone. I've asked people about this and had them remember particular traumatic episodes. Maybe they weren't directly involved, or they just witnessed something or heard about something that ended up being very depressing or upsetting. It's possible that your internal time clock is trying to tell you something when you feel depressed "for no reason." It could also be that you were exposed to a very subtle trigger. Maybe you walked past somebody in a store who vaguely resembled a buddy you lost. Maybe the heat and humidity were just the right combination that day to trigger bad memories. As I said, emotions are not random, so there's almost always a valid reason behind them. Talking to somebody about it can be really helpful in figuring out where the depression is coming from. Once you discover the source, you can do something about it and start to feel better.

WW I, Machine gun battalion, France, 1918, National Archives

Chapter Fourteen

Taps

If you've lost somebody while you were in the war zone, you may not have had any time to deal with it until after you returned home. Even then, you have to readjust to civilian and family life, or just being back in the real world. The trouble is that sometimes while you're going through the post-deployment readjustment stage, the unresolved grief is sometimes bubbling in the background. Maybe the one year anniversary of the loss has already come around. Maybe you're finally starting to relax a little knowing you're not in a war zone anymore. Or maybe it's the first time you're not working as you finally reach retirement age. Either way, as people

Playing Taps, Iraq, 2007, Dept. of Defense

start to relax a little bit and maybe let down some of their defenses, or finally have time to think, the painful memories can frequently begin to rear their ugly heads. If these memories or grief are coming up to the surface while you're still adjusting after you get home, it can make for some pretty tense times at home or at work. People don't understand where your anger is coming from. Some of it may be associated with your grief, which is coming to the surface.

If you had something traumatic happen to you or some of your buddies while you were over there, you may not have been given an opportunity to deal with it emotionally yet. I've talked with people who had friends killed, or were almost killed themselves, but then had to carry on without even taking a break. Like the guy referred to before said, "Just because something blows up, it doesn't mean your day is over." I was talking to one guy who said three of his good friends were killed in an IED (improvised explosive device). They had the memorial service on the FOB (forward operating base) but had to cut it short, because there was a firefight outside the wire. The moment after the memorial service when

Khe Sahn, Vietnam, 1968, Robert Ellison/Empire News

they would've tried to give each other some support and encouragement was cut short. Talk about having to "suck it up and carry on." Sometimes you can't even grieve for your friends.

American Embassy bombing in Beirut, 1983, Dept. of Defense

As many mental health professionals will tell you, there are stages people typically go through with grief. This varies between individuals, but generally they are as follows. When you first see or hear about a death, the typical reaction is "this can't be true, it's not real!" This is the stage when the news is so unacceptable that our brains refuse to acknowledge it. That's the stage of denial. Often times, once the reality sinks in that the death is real, then the anger comes out. The anger stage typically gets us in touch with our outrage that this happened to this particular person. Maybe he or she was so young, or such a good person, or so undeserving of such bad luck. Or maybe you're angry that the person had to die in vain. It's just not fair. If you don't believe in the mission, or you believe that somebody screwed up and made a mistake, you're likely to be really angry about the unnecessary nature of the person's death.

Memorial for Marine killed in Iraq, 2009, Dept. of Defense

On the heels of anger, the sadness frequently sets in. Often this stage of sadness has to be shut down or skipped altogether in a war zone. This is the grieving stage when our sorrow and sense of loss is experienced as sadness. That's when people cry, or wish they could cry. Sometimes the sorrow is so profound or overwhelming that a person's emotions just shut down altogether and he or she feels nothing at all. Don't feel badly about that if that's happened to you. It's like an engine that gets overheated and then just shuts down. Emotions can be like that, too, particularly in such intense situations. Scattered among those very intense stages can be the stage of bargaining. Sometimes people try to bargain with God. "If you spare them I promise to be a good person, or do good deeds, or go to church" or something along those lines.

People frequently have a sense of survivor guilt after somebody they care about dies, particularly in combat. They feel they should've been the one not to make it back. Many times circumstances beyond your control may have resulted in a buddy taking your place on a mission

WW II, Tribute to soldier in France, 1944, National Archives

or in a particular vehicle. I don't know how many times I've heard people say, "I was supposed to be driving the vehicle that day," or "I was supposed to be walking point that day." One of the hardest things to understand about war is why certain people die and others don't. There doesn't seem to be a logical explanation, or at least not one that can satisfy our souls. It just doesn't make sense, and that's what's so hard to accept. Our human brains demand logical explanations for why things happen the way they do. And in tragic circumstances, when there is no explanation we continue to search and search for one.

After people work through some of the emotions and stages of the grief process, many can come to the stage of acceptance. That means you don't like what has happened and it's still painful, but it's not right up in your face all the time. You are able to put the sorrow to the side when you need to. Acceptance doesn't mean that triggers or reminders won't sometimes cause the painful emotions to flare up, but it does mean that it's not always present, interfering with your life all the time.

WW II, American cemetery in Normandy, France

In most societies there are rituals for death, like funerals or memorials. That is traditionally a time when everybody comes together to remember and honor the life of the person who has died. It's a time when those who loved or cared about the person can share their memories and grieve together. They can offer one another support in a way that outsiders cannot. Friends and family come together to talk, cry, laugh, reminisce and heal. On the battlefield this is not the case. Many have put a buddy on a chopper, never knowing if he made it or not. For many, their friend was there one minute, and the next minute he or she was gone. The fragility of life is driven home in a very harsh way. The first time you have a buddy wounded or killed, your emotions shut down. Some people react with raw pain and grief when it happens. Some people are just numb, like in the denial stage. Either way, you learn that emotion is not your friend in war. It compromises your ability to survive and can cloud your judgment. This is "one trial learning." In other words, it only takes one time before you learn to ignore or totally detach from your emotions. Since you're usually not allowed the opportunity of a real funeral in a war zone,

Memorial, Iraq, 2007, Dept. of Defense

you're left with some unfinished business. It's hard to lose somebody you care about even in the best of situations. It's just that much harder when you lose somebody under the really stressful and difficult situation like war.

It's even harder to lose somebody when you've developed the close, tight knit bonds that develop amongst warriors on the battlefield. These are the people you trust with your life, to watch your back. And you watch their back. The loyalty is unparalleled and irreplaceable. That's another reason it's so traumatic when one of them dies or is wounded. This is your brother or sister whom you've

Sweeping for mines, DMZ, Vietnam, 1967, Robert Ellison/Empire News

sworn to protect, even if it means putting your own life at risk. Unfortunately, there are so many circumstances beyond your control in a war zone. We try our best to be prepared and anticipate and control. Things don't always go according to plan. There are things you can't control, and that are unforeseen, for which you can't prepare. IEDs or booby traps are the perfect examples of this. You try your best to detect and be constantly on guard for the unforeseen. But the thing that makes them so deadly is the hidden, unexpected, surprise nature of these guerilla tactics. It's part of what makes you so angry when something so unpredictable and uncontrollable like this strikes. Somehow you think you should've been able to prevent it on every occasion. The human condition makes it impossible for anybody to catch it every time.

The cost of not being able to detect them is extremely high. It's the price of human life and limb.

Khe Sahn, Vietnam, 1968, Robert Ellison/Empire News

There is another factor that complicates grief in war. In most societies, people are particularly traumatized when a young person dies, especially if it's violent and sudden. It doesn't make sense in the cycle of life. Young people are not supposed to die before old people. Life doesn't work that way. When an older person dies, it's still sad, but at least they had an opportunity to live their life. When a young person dies, he or she is robbed of his or her entire future, and of his or her potential. However, we send our young people to war, not our old. They are stronger, more resilient, and able to endure more hardships by virtue of their youth. So war involves the sudden, violent death of the young. These are frequently the brightest stars with the most promise. It seems like it always happens to the best people, too. The unfairness of it is gut wrenching and tragic. The young people often have children of their own as they're beginning their own families. This makes it even harder to tolerate or understand. Not only are they being deprived of their future potential, but their children are being deprived of their parent also.

Khe Sahn, Vietnam, 1968, Robert Ellison/Empire News

Guilt is a common feeling when one of your people gets killed. Sometimes it's appropriate, because somebody screwed up or wasn't paying attention when he or she was supposed to. Sometimes the intelligence information was faulty. Sometimes the orders were bad. Unfortunately, many people blame themselves, even if there really wasn't anything they could've done to prevent the death or injury. We can't control the uncontrollable. We can't know the unknown. But we refuse to accept that fact, because the cost is so high. It's unacceptable that we can't be perfect and prevent tragedy. It's not fair.

Memorial service in Iraq, 2007, Dept. of Defense

"It should have been me instead of him." I can't tell you how many times I have I heard people say that. Due to some fluke, like a random change in your position or assignment, you almost got killed but didn't. The other guy was in your place somehow and ended up getting killed. It should've been you, but it wasn't. How do you make sense of something like that? There are no easy answers. Some people believe it's random. Some people believe they were spared for a reason and feel a sense of duty to make their lives count for something in a good way. Other people suffer with the guilt feelings for most of their lives. This is part of why war is hell.

Khe Sahn, Vietnam, 1968, Robert Ellison/Empire News

Some people who suffer guilt feel they have to punish themselves. They feel that by whipping themselves for their role in the tragedy, they are somehow paying restitution. They feel that healing from the grief would be disloyal or inappropriate. However, self-forgiveness and compassion are some of the most important, yet most elusive, principles to incorporate in order to begin the healing process. If you have a photo of yourself at the age when you went to war, take a good hard look at it. Look at how young and inexperienced you really were. Particularly if it was the first time you went to war, you had no idea what to expect. You may have had a lot of training, but nothing could've truly prepared you for what you were going to experience in combat. If that photo was of another young man or woman, you would probably have more compassion for him or her than you do for yourself. That young person did the best he or she could under the severe duress and chaos of combat, so cut him or her some slack. You probably would for a stranger, so try to do it for yourself.

Cordon and search operation, Kirkuk, Iraq, 2010, Dept. of Defense

When you stop to think about the actual training and preparation you had for combat, it probably wasn't really enough to totally prepare you for the real thing. So you go on missions with the amount of training and equipment and experience you have or don't have. You do the best you can under the circumstances. You, as one individual, only have control over a small amount of what happens in combat. There are many, many factors beyond your control, so don't overestimate the degree of control you think you should've had. Remember, hindsight is always 20/20, so it's easy to think about how you should or could have done things differently from the safety of your life away from a combat zone. People remember the facts of the combat experience through the filters of chaos, distorted senses, adrenalin and youth. That does not usually capture all the facts and aspects of the event. Most people only remember what their senses were taking in under severe duress.

Remembering Sept. 11th, Afghanistan, 2010, Dept. of Defense

That's not an accurate enough picture of all of the extenuating circumstances and factors involved to be able to pass judgment on how you handled the situation at the time. This is one of the reasons it is so important to process and discuss the details of the combat experience with a trusted counselor. Filling in the details between the "snapshots" of memories is critical to really be able to evaluate how you reacted. So, before you pass harsh judgment on yourself and feel too guilty about your actions, think about talking to a counselor or trusted buddy about it. You wouldn't pass judgment on anybody else without having all the facts, so don't do it to yourself.

"Real warriors don't cry." Think again. Most men and women who have been in combat, particularly if they've lost somebody, do cry. And if the tears won't come, they want to cry but can't let it out. The bonds that develop in combat with your buddies are stronger than any you'll probably develop the rest of your life. Once you've trusted somebody with protecting your life and been willing to give your life to protect theirs, the trust doesn't get any deeper than that. When something tragic happens and that person's life is taken in a split

WW II, wounded Marines towed on rubber boats, National Archives

second, your life will never be the same. You now know what it's like to lose a brother or sister. Death is a reality for you now. The feelings can be overwhelming. So much so, that sometimes there is only shock or disbelief in the beginning. It can't be true. He or she was here a minute ago and now he or she is gone. After the initial shock wears off, the horror and rage can kick in, sometimes sooner rather than later. These are activating, energizing emotions that motivate you to take action, seek justice or revenge. There is usually no room for the sadness, tears and grief while still in a combat or war zone. The focus has to be on the mission and your own survival. There is no luxury for grieving and mourning. That has to wait until later.

It's usually only later on that the sadness really surfaces. Sometimes it's when you get home. Sometimes it's thirty years later before you allow yourself to truly grieve. Everybody handles it differently. Whenever the emotional pain surfaces for you, the tears are usually just below the surface. The military culture requires, out of necessity, that you just "suck it up and push on." However, there comes a point at which that's no longer the best course of action. At some time or another the sadness will make itself heard. It might come out in nightmares or flashbacks. It might come bursting into your consciousness while you're working on a project around your house or at work. It might come out around the holidays as you think about the families who will be trying to celebrate without their loved one. Grief and sorrow will make themselves known, whether we like it or not.

Memorial at FOB Delta, Iraq, 2009, Dept. of Defense

If you're actively struggling with grief or guilt related to a death, talking to a counselor or clergy member can be tremendously helpful. If dealing with the grief was something that was easy for people to do on their own, they would've done it already and not still be struggling with it. Death in combat results in a very tragic and complicated grief to deal with. There is no shame in asking for guidance and assistance when you're grieving the death of a brother or sister. Only honor and respect for his or her memory.

Khe Sahn, Vietnam, 1968, Robert Ellison/Empire News

CHAPTER FIFTEEN

Nights Are The Worst

Most combat veterans have had to sleep with one ear and one eye open in the combat zone. It's "stay alert, stay alive." When a skill is necessary for your survival, it becomes like a reflex and is automatic. Automatic reflexes like that are so deeply ingrained that your "auto pilot" keeps running even while you're asleep. Your brain continues to monitor the noises in your surroundings and wakes up at intervals to make sure it's still safe. Most combat veterans wake up multiple times during the night and are very light sleepers, if they sleep much at all. Many do perimeter checks around their homes during the night as well, "just to be sure." Kind of sounds like guard duty, doesn't it? Some people will wake up at almost exactly the same time every night. If you stop and think about it, that time probably meant something to you in the war zone.

Combats Outpost Munoz, Afghanistan, 2009, Dept. of Defense

Maybe it was time for your shift on guard duty. Maybe it was the time you got mortared a lot. It's that subconscious internal time clock people have. When it's a life or death situation, those reflexes become deeply ingrained. Your brain is on alert status even while you're asleep.

Roof top extraction in Baghdad, Iraq, 2004, Dept. of Defense

It's not uncommon for people to have nightmares after they've been through a really traumatic event. Often they are reenactments of the event itself. Other times they're reenactments of the emotions associated with the event. Dreams and nightmares are the mind's way of working through problems. It's how we try to make sense of things or work through issues while we're asleep. Our subconscious mind kind of takes over and tries to take care of business through conflict resolution. It tries to fix a problem we find unacceptable. For example, it is unacceptable that such a good person should've been killed. It makes no sense. Our mind continues to search, even while it's asleep, for a way to make the situation have a good ending or outcome. We find it unacceptable that it should have happened the way it really did. Unfortunately, war is full of

Khe Sahn, Vietnam, 1968, Robert Ellison/Empire News

"no-win" situations. Many times there is no good outcome no matter what you do. Either you kill or get killed. That leaves unfinished business. As far as many traumatic events are concerned, the mind finds it absolutely unacceptable that such a tragedy could take place. The subconscious mind refuses to accept that something so horrific or life-threatening could really have taken place. Dreams are a magical place where things don't have to be logical or make sense. So the mind keeps trying to play the event over and over again in hopes of having a different outcome, a better outcome.

Nightmares are a form of conflict resolution, but there is no resolution or way of undoing the trauma you experienced. It was so unacceptable that your brain keeps trying to fix it. The typical belief is that if you're capable you're supposed to be able to fix the situation and solve the problems. So what do you do when the situation is a no-win? Your conscious brain tells you to move on, there's nothing you can do about it. But your unconscious brain refuses to accept that. It tells you the situation and the

Sniper in Iraq, 2004, Dept. of Defense

outcome are not acceptable, so you need to keep trying to fix it, even if it's unfixable. Isn't that what the mission calls for? Failure is not an option, so keep trying until you find a solution or an acceptable outcome. That's another reason why war is hell. Many of the situations in which you find yourself have no easy solution or just can't be fixed.

If an actual traumatic event involves you feeling trapped or helpless, then your nightmares may reflect those emotions instead of the actual event. That's your mind's way of trying to resolve those feelings and fix the problem. It keeps hoping that if it just tries hard enough it will have a happier ending, and you won't feel so

Iraq, 2003, Dept. of Defense

helpless or trapped. Recurrent dreams or nightmares are your mind's way of trying to let you know what issues are unresolved. It's sending you messages in the only way it knows how about the unfinished business that needs to be taken care of. That's why I say the only way to get to the other side is to go through. These dreams and nightmares will continue until you go ahead and take the bull by the horns and confront the issues. Many times after having talked about a traumatic event in detail, a person will experience a sense of relief. He or she has filled in the blanks and now has a complete picture of what actually occurred. It can help you make sense to some degree out of what happened.

The memory you have before you talk it through is somewhat distorted. Your brain has encoded the information through your eighteen year old eyes while you were under severe stress. There's no way you've accurately recalled the details and facts about what happened. All you remember is what was filtered through at the time.

Iraq, 2003, Dept. of Defense

Again, this is why it's so important to get an accurate picture. You may be feeling guilty about not having performed a mission properly. Sometimes, by going back over the factual details, you can figure out why a mistake occurred or may find that you didn't really make a mistake at all. Something else could have been going on that distracted you. Maybe you were so good at doing your job that you did it on autopilot just the way you'd been trained. In other words, recreating the scene can provide critical factual information that changes your interpretation of how you acted or didn't act at the time. A classic example is the medic who blamed himself for not reacting quickly enough, only to realize that the reason he didn't was because they were being attacked from both sides at the same time. It was physically impossible for him to be 100% focused on what was happening on either side of him and his patient at the same time during the ambush.

In dreams or nightmares the content can feel so real that the body reacts as if it's actually happening again. Many people describe waking up drenched in sweat. Sometimes they wake up with a sudden start. Often they thrash around in the bed, even accidentally hitting their partner or falling out of the bed. This is the physiological stress reaction that occurs resulting in all the stress hormones firing, even while you're asleep. Frequently people will wake up feeling terrified or angry or startled. This is the emotional reaction to the dream content. That's how real a nightmare or dream can seem. I don't know how many people have told me that their spouse

Operation Soprano Sunset, Baghdad, Iraq, 2004, Dept. of Defense

sleeps in a different room because of all their thrashing around, calling out, yelling, and so forth, all of which they do while they're asleep.

As more veterans are getting psychological help with their nightmares, medicine is developing new treatments as well. Clinical practice and research have discovered that there are certain medications that can actually help control nightmares. They don't work for everybody, but they have been shown to be helpful for a lot of people. Talk to your doctor, preferably a psychiatrist, about this. Sleep aids are helpful to some people as well. Medications in this arena sometimes require a little trial and error in terms of dosages or which medication to use. So, if the first medication you try doesn't help, don't give up. Just talk to your doctor about it so he or she can adjust the dose or try something different. Your doctor isn't treating you like a guinea pig. Not all medicines work the same for all people. It can be a very individualized thing that requires some adjustments and patience. Don't underestimate the importance of a good night's sleep. You're

Thanksgiving in Baghdad, Iraq, 2006

probably so used to not feeling refreshed in the morning that you've forgotten what it feels like. If it's a problem, talk to your doctor.

Another issue to be aware of is sleep apnea. If your spouse tells you that you stop breathing while you're asleep, or that you gasp for air or snore, discuss it with your doctor. Sleep apnea can play a big role in war veterans not getting enough sleep. This can contribute to irritability, depression and decreased concentration. Sleep studies are usually required to determine if you have a disorder like sleep apnea. There's no need to suffer if there's something like a CPAP machine that can help you sleep better. Your doctor should be able to determine if further evaluation is necessary.

CHAPTER SIXTEEN

Holidays Suck

Why is it that everybody tries to act like the holidays are always so perfect and happy? The media and the retailers are the worst about that. Everywhere you look there are pictures of perfect, happy people with perfect, happy lives. They're on commercials and advertisements everywhere. None of those people look like they have bills to pay or difficult family members to deal with at the holidays. Who do they think they are, acting like they don't have a care in the world?! Don't they know that there are people starving and dying in other parts of the world at this very minute? Even right here in America too. The conspicuous consumption of Americans is at its peak during the holidays. The unrealistic expectations of what perfect families are supposed to be are thrown in our faces at

Christmas Eve, Iraq, 2007, Dept. of Defense

every turn. It's the ultimate example of "ignorance is bliss." Whoever these perfect people are, they've obviously never had to go to war and leave their family behind, celebrate a holiday in a war zone with crappy food, or think about their buddy who won't get the chance to celebrate another holiday with his or her family.

Vietnam, 1965, National Archives

Once you've been to war, the whole holiday concept gets a little warped from what it was when you were a kid. The misery and suffering of others that you've witnessed, even at those special times of the year, overshadows and contaminates the fantasy of the perfect holiday. That's not to say that it can't also make you really appreciate being home with your family for a holiday again. Once you've witnessed or experienced hard times or acute loneliness during the holidays, it can make you appreciate what you have just that much more once you get back home. However, there's usually that bittersweet feeling in the background. You can't forget what you've seen and where you've been. Holidays can spark an "anniversary reaction" of sorts. When the particular holiday rolls around this year, it naturally reminds you of where you were during this holiday in the past years. Some of those memories aren't that pleasant. Some are downright painful. Even though a holiday in combat is just another day, the calendar date is still the same.

WW II, Battle of the Bulge, 1945, National Archives

Many combat veterans have a dislike for the holidays. It can be hard for their families to understand. Your family hasn't been where you have during the holidays. That's not to say that they didn't have their own hardships while you were gone to a war zone. They missed you and were worried about you. They made a lot of sacrifices too. Maybe they're so grateful to have you home for this holiday that in their minds their gratitude overshadows everything else. If that's the case, you can see how different the two perspectives are. You can also see how there can be hurt feelings and misunderstandings if both parties don't understand where the other one is coming from. This is why communication is so important.

Christmas Eve in Baghdad, Iraq, 2006, Dept. of Defense

You don't have to go into the gory details with your spouse about your bad holiday experiences. Hopefully, trying to explain what it was like for you during a holiday in the war zone will help them understand why it's hard for you now. If you lost somebody in combat around the time of a holiday, it's natural to understand that the particular date or time of the year may stir up painful memories for you. If you saw people suffering at this time of the year, that memory may have become associated with the holiday in your mind. There is no way for your family members to fully understand your feelings and thoughts about this, but at least it gives them an opportunity to try to imagine what it might have been like for you. If you don't explain to them why you're feeling depressed or irritable or down in the dumps at the holidays, then it's not really being fair to them. If you don't at least try to explain it, they're likely to assume that it's something they did or didn't do, or that you're just being ornery or difficult. Maybe letting them read this book will help explain some of it, or at least let them know it's not just you who reacts this way. This is a very common reaction that many combat veterans experience. It happens for a valid reason, and you're not alone.

Operation Oregon, Vietnam, 1966, National Archives

CHAPTER SEVENTEEN

There Are No Atheists In Foxholes

War frequently has a profound effect on a person's beliefs and spirituality. It can go one of two ways.

Religious service in bunker, Khe Sahn, Vietnam, 1968, Robert Ellison/Empire News

If you were raised in a home where the Ten Commandments or other spiritual guidelines were important, it can cause some serious conflicts for you in war. The military doesn't usually prepare you for how to deal with moral dilemmas or spiritual wounds. The most obvious example is "Thou shalt not kill." How do you get around that one in combat? This is easier for some people than for others. When it comes right down to it, you don't have a lot of choices when the situation is either you kill them or they're going to kill you. You do what you have to do to survive. But that doesn't mean that the issue of guilt may not come back at some point down the road. This is where talking to a chaplain or member of the clergy comes in handy. It's a complicated issue for many people, and there are no easy answers. The key issue is forgiveness either self-forgiveness or forgiveness from your higher power if you have one.

Death, or near-death experiences, in war often impact your beliefs about the existence or nature of God or a higher power. Some people become convinced that God was with them every step of the way, helping them stay alive. I've talked to people who have described what they literally refer to as "miracles." They feel as if God's hand reached down and moved them to a different position from where they would have surely been killed. These kinds of experiences usually strengthen a person's spiritual beliefs.

Civil War Chaplain conducting service, 1861, National Archives

However, the deaths of friends, particularly if they were unnecessary, can cause people to question the existence of God. Sometimes they ask themselves how an almighty Creator could exist and allow those tragedies to happen. They struggle with what kind of a being God could be to stand by and watch innocent children die. Sometimes people feel as if their God has abandoned them. The despair and pain they feel is so overwhelming that they feel God has forsaken them. These are painful struggles that many people go through.

I know guys who carried Bibles and religious medals into combat with them. Many warriors attended religious services right before going out to kill and destroy. Either way you look at it, the love and tolerance espoused by most religions is not consistent with war and killing. It can be pretty much an impossible situation.

Operations Hastings, Vietnam, 1966, National Archives

Sometimes people experience a sense of loss and grief over losing the person they were raised to be. If their family expected them to abide by religious and spiritual guidelines, which they were unable to do in war, they feel like they've somehow failed. It can be an untenable situation. You are asked to betray some of your own beliefs out of necessity for your own survival. If that's not a catch-22, no-win situation, I don't know what is.

The only thing I can say is this: If some psychologist like me can comprehend the moral dilemma and impossible nature of the situation, I'm quite certain the Almighty Creator can grasp it, too. If you believe in a higher power, then you probably believe that he or she is pretty omnipotent, or all-knowing, or something along those lines. If that's the case, then you kind of have to assume that God already knows the impossible situation you were in and understands it. If I can cut you some slack for it, thenI'm quite sure God can. If he and I can do it, then you should probably cut yourself some slack and forgive yourself, too.

Priest celebrating mass, Vietnam, 1967,
Paul Stephanus/Empire News

What about your own mortality? Most civilians assume they'll live a long healthy life and grow old. Combat veterans know that's not a given. People are not guaranteed to live even another day. You know that people can die at any moment. Death is real for you, particularly if you have cheated death yourself. If you've come close to losing your life, you know you're not as invincible as you once might have thought you were. Many combat veterans who have been in harm's way have a sense that they may not live as long as other people. If you've already cheated death on several occasions, then you think that maybe you've used up all your luck. Maybe the odds are stacked against you. You are the one who chooses what to do with that information and how you let it affect the way you lead your life. Some people find that very depressing and discouraging. Others choose to live their lives to the fullest and appreciate whatever time they have on this earth. One man said he felt it was his obligation to live the best life he could, since he made it back when so many did not. He felt he owed it to those who were killed on the battlefield to be the best person he could be. That's the ultimate example of choosing to make something positive come out of tragedy. Food for thought.

Chapter Eighteen

Killing

Most human beings are originally repulsed by the idea of killing, whether it's having to put down a pet or kill someone in battle. The very nature of war involves killing the enemy. It's a given requirement of battle. It often comes down to "kill or be killed." It often involves obtaining justice for the wrongs that have been perpetrated by the enemy. The training you received and the values you incorporated were ultimately directed toward the mission of defeating the enemy, by killing them or capturing them.

WW II, Battle of Saipan, 1944, National Archives

As I mentioned when talking about grief, most people go through stages when they have to kill another human being. Lt. Col. Dave Grossman identifies these stages in his book "On Killing." These stages vary among people and can be different in terms of which stages somebody experiences, or even skips altogether. There is no "right way" to react to the experience of killing. Initially, many people worry about whether they'll actually be able to go through with it when the time comes. There can often be a fear of not being able to go through with it in a critical moment, or of freezing up. This could result in your own death or the death of one of your buddies, so it's a legitimate concern or fear.

Afghanistan, 2010, Dept. of Defense

The actual experience of killing somebody, pulling the trigger, is very quick and often like a reflex which was learned during training. It happens very quickly and frequently while you're under fire, in the adrenalin rush of the moment. Hopefully, the training and preparation kick in automatically. However, sometimes people freeze up. This is nothing to be ashamed of, as it does happen sometimes. Stop and think about the chaos, the adrenalin, the fear or anger, the natural repulsion to killing, and never actually having done it before. It's not all that surprising that people freeze up when the moment of truth actually arrives. It appears to be a very simple action, but is actually surrounded by a lot of psychological complications and input that can overwhelm the system. So if you've ever frozen up, don't beat yourself up about it. There are good reasons why it can happen to the bravest of warriors.

WW II, Iwo Jima, 1944, National Archives

Once you've killed a combatant, there is often a sense of satisfaction or feeling of exhilaration. All of your training has led up to this moment. The purpose of the mission in war usually is to get rid of the enemy before he gets rid of you first. You have accomplished the goal after all the build up and expectations. The adrenalin rush that comes along with the experience can give people an incredible high, and an intense feeling of power. There are few things so intense. This is why some people actually become addicted to the adrenalin rush high of killing. The positive sensations seem to be more easily experienced by those who kill at a medium or long range, rather than at close range. However, most people don't talk about it, because it is socially unacceptable to those who have never experienced it. Sometimes you are even rewarded and congratulated for killing, and thereby accomplishing the mission. I knew somebody who said in Vietnam that their Lt. said they would be rewarded for their first kill by being allowed to grow a moustache. How often have your buddies congratulated you when you "got the bad guys?" It's the values and reactions of the group of people you're with at the time that can strongly influence your own reaction.

Vietnam, National Archives

After the smoke has cleared and the dust has settled, people can experience an intense feeling of remorse or shame. This is particularly true with a close range kill. The horror of seeing the results of taking another human being's life can be overwhelming. The realization of what has occurred can be traumatic. This is one of the reasons most combatants become emotionally cold and hard. It would be impossible to kill again if you allowed yourself to fully experience the intense negative emotions every time you had to do it. Your system would become overwhelmed, and your survival would be in jeopardy. This is why the ability to totally shut off your emotions develops so quickly and thoroughly. It allows you to do your job and survive. Just like so many other coping skills learned at an early age in war, it becomes part of your make-up. This is also why so many have no feelings when they pass an automobile accident or hear about a murder on the news, etc.

WW II, National Archives

Often times in war there are no good choices. You're screwed no matter which choice you make. It's either kill or be killed. That's a little more straightforward if you're fighting enemy soldiers, but not so straightforward when there are civilians, especially children, involved. Not such an easy decision when one of your own people will die no matter whether you choose to go left or you choose to go right. There are so many no-win situations in war that it can be overwhelming. Maybe you can think more clearly now that the danger is over and you're evaluating the action afterward. Have compassion for that younger man or woman who had less experience and was pumped with adrenalin and survival instincts. Remember that the reflexes and instincts and training take over. You make the best call you can in the heat of the moment based on the information you have and the information you don't have. So cut yourself some slack and have a little compassion for yourself. We all tend to hold ourselves to higher standards than we do others. You can't afford to do that to yourself in war. The rules aren't the same. If you're going to pass judgment on yourself, you have to tell the whole truth and nothing but the truth. You have to take into account all the factors involved, including being scared, angry, pumped with adrenalin, and in automatic training mode. You do the best you know how to do in the heat of the battle. End of story.

WW I, cannon firing, National Archives

Most warriors are left trying to make sense of a split-second decision and an action of killing for the rest of their lives. Being able to come to terms with this is easier for some people than for others. Some people never come to a place of being okay with what they've done. Others are able to rationalize that what they did was necessary and the only appropriate choice at the time. Some people struggle with feelings of guilt and remorse for the rest of their lives. This can be particularly true for those who felt they "enjoyed" killing at the time they were in the war zone, but then regret it later on.

Warriors are trained to depersonalize their enemies. This is most frequently done by giving them nicknames like "Gooks, Krauts, Hajis," etc. This objectifies the enemy and takes away their humanity. It degrades them so that they are not "one of us" any longer. It solidifies the "us against them" nature of war. It makes it more acceptable to kill somebody we don't identify with as another human being of equal value. Sometimes, as the years pass and the questions about the reason for the war come to the surface, this rationalization can fade. This can make the guilt feelings rise to the surface. Questions like "Why didn't I see that they were individuals trying to protect their homeland?" can erupt.

Iraq door gunner, 2010, Dept. of Defense

Photo # SC 347107 Army 105mm howitzer crew in action, Korea, Aug. 1950

Howitzer, Korea, 1950, National Archives

The issue of killing by mistake, like in friendly fire situations, can be particularly devastating. The bonds of brotherhood you have with your comrades can be one of the strongest you'll ever have in your life. You are there to protect your fellow warriors, and they are there to protect you. It's "us against them." So when there is an accidental death by friendly fire, it feels like a betrayal of your brother or sister. It often doesn't make sense. The good guys aren't supposed to die, especially not that way. It's bad enough if one of your own is killed by the enemy. It's even worse if they're killed by another one of your own people. It's one of those tragic things that does occur in war. Mistakes are made, and accidents happen. It is unacceptable, but unfortunately it's also reality. It isn't right, and it isn't fair. It isn't supposed to happen that way. That's why it's so hard to understand or make sense of it when it does occur. The guilt can be overwhelming if you've been involved in an incident like this. Please talk to a counselor, chaplain, or trusted friend about this if you have been involved. The issues of forgiveness for yourself and from God are crucial for the healing to begin. If you've witnessed a death by friendly fire, your anger and grief can be extremely intense. This is something you shouldn't have to deal with by yourself, whether you were directly involved or just witnessed it.

Stryker Brigade Combat Team, Iraq, 2004, Dept. of Defense

It's important to look at the culture and training you experienced in preparation for war. Depersonalization of the enemy and feeling good about killing are necessary for anybody to go into combat and kill. Your own sense of survival is also necessary, as well as the need to watch your buddies' backs and not let anything happen to them. You are bound by honor and duty to protect and defend your own and wipe out the enemy. This becomes your primary concern and way of behaving. Humans have a natural need for justice and vengeance when one of their own is killed or maimed. The anger can be overwhelming and fuel the desire to kill the enemy. This is when many war crimes are committed and the satisfaction from the kill can be the strongest. I have heard many individuals talk about their regrets about having "gone too far" in the heat of the moment. It didn't seem like the violence they committed was too much at the time. Sometimes, after the fact, when the emotions have faded, the acts of vengeance taken can leave feelings of shame and remorse.

Hopefully, people can come to the stage of acceptance, where they have made peace with the actions they took in war. Sometimes it's possible to reach total acceptance, although for many finding partial acceptance is the best they can achieve. Finding a degree of acceptance for yourself and what you have done can be a lifelong struggle. One of the most important concepts involved is self-forgiveness, and forgiveness from God or your higher power if you have one. In most religions, forgiveness is yours for the asking as long as you have a sincere heart and desire to be forgiven. If this is an issue with which you are struggling, please talk to a chaplain, priest, rabbi, or spiritual leader of your choosing. You are not the only one struggling for forgiveness, and they can provide guidance and comfort.

Combat Outpost Michigan, Afghanistan, 2010, Dept. of Defense

Mosul Iraq, 2003, Dept. of Defense

If you are struggling more with self-forgiveness, then compassion is the place to start. We typically hold ourselves to higher standards than we hold others. Somehow we feel we should always be able to take the high road or avoid the common mistakes and pitfalls made by others. We feel we "should've known better." So we judge ourselves more harshly than we judge others. The truth is that most of us do the best we can in any given situation... given the resources, knowledge, skills, strength and awareness that we have or don't have at the time. Hindsight is always 20/20. We can always see more clearly and logically after the heat of the moment is gone. We can always make more rational, reasonable choices or decisions after the fact. By the time we're passing judgments on ourselves, we're usually older and wiser and know better. That's the whole point. You cannot pass judgment on your younger, less experienced self. It doesn't make any sense to hold your younger self to the standards you hold for yourself now. It's illogical. That's why it's important to develop some compassion for your younger self.

One of the ways I assist people in accomplishing this is having them find a photograph of themselves when they were the age at which they went to war. Look at how young and relatively inexperienced that young person is. Think about kids nowadays who are the same age and think about how mature or immature they act. Imagine them being in the impossible situations or faced with the no-win decisions of war. It's not a very pretty picture, is it? If you look at it from that perspective, a lot of times you'll be amazed at how maturely and responsibly you acted in spite of your age. The other way to have more compassion for your younger self is to imagine some young person who just returned from war today describing his or her own reactions to situations you faced.

Khe Sahn, Vietnam, 1968, Robert Ellison/Empire News

You would probably have more understanding and compassion for the younger person than you do for yourself. You would most likely judge him or her less harshly than you have judged yourself. You might tell him he did the best he could under the circumstances. You might tell her that she didn't have enough experience to know what to do in the situation. You would probably cut him or her a lot more slack than you do yourself. Maybe you're being too hard on yourself. This is where talking to a counselor or spiritual leader can also be very helpful. This is not an easy internal struggle to have. It typically causes a lot of anguish and costs a lot of emotional energy to wage this internal war with yourself. You don't have to do it alone. Talk to somebody about it.

Huey firing a rocket, DMZ, Vietnam, 1967, Robert Ellison/Empire News

In his book "On Combat" Lt. Col. Dave Grossman identifies a vital difference essential to understanding guilt about killing in war. He talks about the difference between "Thou shalt not kill" versus "Thou shalt not murder." If you have to kill in the line of duty fighting for what you believe to be necessary and right, then that is not considered to be murder. That is considered to be killing. If you kill another human being to protect your own life or your buddies' then that is not murder. Murder is considered to be taking another person's life to obtain some personal gain or benefit, whether it's material or psychological in nature. It is not necessary for a greater good. This is a very important difference recognized by most religions. If psychologists and spiritual leaders can recognize and determine the differences between those two concepts, then God or a higher power already knew the differences before you went to war. God or your higher power already knows what is in your mind and heart. He recognizes your remorse, regret, shame, pain, anger, guilt, and sadness. Forgiveness is already yours if you desire it sincerely.

Khe Sahn, Vietnam, 1968, Robert Ellison/Empire News

I've heard a lot of warriors talk about the futility of the deaths they witnessed on the battle field. They've spoken about how many lives were lost and asked what the purpose was in the end. Many have wondered, "What did the deaths accomplish?" This can be particularly difficult when the country in which you fought has gone right back to the way it was before you even got there. Vietnam is a good example. At least with WW II, the many lives lost were justified for the end result of freedom. Many ask the same questions about the wars in Iraq and Afghanistan, "What will these wars accomplish in the long run?" It is particularly difficult for those who are struggling with those questions as they are on the battle field or contemplating their 3rd or 4th deployment. This is one of the issues that can make coping with life after war difficult, particularly when you reach middle age and beyond.

Iraq, 2004, Dept. of Defense

We begin to question and examine the meaning of our lives and our purpose on earth. We begin to think more about the afterlife and the legacy we've left behind. This is a natural stage for most people, but war and killing make these existential questions more complex and difficult to resolve for warriors. That's why so many people finally go to talk to a counselor or spiritual leader about their internal struggles with coping with their war experiences. A lifetime of struggling with these issues becomes very burdensome and isolating. There are no easy answers, but at least if you talk to someone experienced in dealing with these issues then you won't be trying to re-invent the wheel by yourself. There is healing to be had.

Khe Sahn, Vietnam, 1968, Robert Ellison/Empire News

Chapter Nineteen

We Were Never There

The people, and you know who you are, who were officially never in places like Laos, Cambodia, Nicaragua, Columbia, and others have a unique burden to bear. Anybody involved in covert operations, Special Forces, or Black Ops is in the untenable position of not being able to talk about what they did and where they were. If you were with a team then at least you got to debrief with them after the mission was over. If you were on missions with other units or only brought together for a specific mission or worked solo, then you were deprived of that opportunity. Even if you did get to debrief right after a mission, what about after you're back home again

Navy SEALS Operation Just Cause, Panama, 1989, Dept. of Defense

or out of the military? You've been trained to not talk. The safety of the missions, your buddies, and yourself depend upon you keeping your mouth shut. End of story. So how is that supposed to work when you get home and your spouse wants to talk and communicate? Not so well. Even in counseling that can be a challenge. If your life depended on your secrecy, then it's pretty hard to leave it at the door.

It's a dilemma, but not insurmountable. It's still possible to be able to talk about your reactions to situations without betraying classified information. If you're describing how treacherous and scary the jungle can be and how that has contributed to your hypervigilance, that doesn't betray any state secrets. But it does help your family understand why you're so jumpy sometimes. Try to explain the need for tolerating no mistakes, no room for error, and "failure is not an option." Those things which are required for survival on missions don't just disappear once you get home. Those expectations

Navy SEALS Vietnam, 1967, National Archives

stay with you, your expectations both of yourself and of others. Explaining why you think and behave that way can help your family understand why you get so bent out of shape over seemingly little things at times. Trying to explain the level of hyperawareness and preparedness which your life depended on is important. If you haven't experienced it, you can't fully comprehend how much adrenalin is involved. But at least they can try to imagine it and take that into account in trying to understand why you're wired so tight at times or such a perfectionist.

WW II, Kwajalein, 1944, National Archives

Explaining the need for total security and safety to your family can also be helpful. It helps them understand why you're always checking the perimeter or getting so upset if somebody forgets to lock the door or the car. It helps explain why you appear to be "paranoid" or "overprotective" at times. In the world you come from it's just good business practice to be extra careful and suspicious. It can, and probably did, save your life. Your family needs to understand that your concern or focus on security issues is based on your own real life experience. You have seen evil and looked it in the face. You know the worst in people. Those who have not been to war usually only think about those dangers in an abstract way. They figure it's something that happens to other people or in movies. It's appropriate at this point to say that "ignorance truly is bliss."

E.O.D. in DaNang, Vietnam, 1966, National Archives

Most people don't realize how lucky they are that they don't really know how dangerous a place the world can be. Most people don't realize how lucky they are that death and destruction haven't touched their lives directly. That's why it's so important to educate them about your own experiences. Let them know that danger and threats are part of your personal history. It's a reality for you. So ask them to bear with you on this one. By the same token, please try to bear with them when they don't take it as seriously as you would like them to. How would they know about the dangers you do? It's not part of their history usually, so explain it to them. All this can be done without betraying confidential information. Try to remember that not talking was critical back then, but that being able to talk is critical now.

Going on covert missions, whether you are Special Forces or have worked with them, frequently involves leaving your identity behind. Sometimes you have to be without any information that might identify you as even an American. You have to sometimes even be willing to let your country deny your existence. That's real dedication and loyalty. Going into danger knowing your family may never really know what happened to you is true commitment. It's commitment on your part as well as on your family's part. That takes a toll on people. Even though you know you've been chosen because you're the best of the best, you also know the stakes are usually even higher, otherwise they wouldn't be sending you. Not having identification is an extra level of vulnerability that can make the experiences more harrowing. You know you can't count on the military to come and bail you out. You're on your own. That raises the stakes even higher. Failure is definitely not an option.

Special Forces insertion with canine, Iraq, 2010, Dept. of Defense

If you've gone through Special Forces training and it's what you signed up for, then at least you sort of know what you're getting yourself into. Again, no training can probably truly prepare you for the real deal, but it sure helps. Many times there are support personnel who accompany or work closely with Special Forces. It's not always exactly what they signed up for. Usually somebody chose them because they're really good at what they do. It can be thrilling to work that closely with the elite, but it can also be unnerving. There are dog handlers who get recruited to go on covert missions with Special Forces teams. There are Marines who end up searching cargo vessels with Navy SEALS. There are the people who are involved in insertions and extractions. No pressure there. All of these extra responsibilities and stress levels, whether you expect them or not, can make traumatic situations just that much more difficult to process and deal with. It's another layer to be dealt with. All the more reason to talk to somebody about the challenges unique to Special Forces and those who work closely with them.

WW II, K-9's on Iwo Jima, National Archives

Chapter Twenty

A League of Their Own: Medics and Corpsmen

Hero's Highway, Balad, Iraq, 2009, Dept. of Defense

Most medics and corpsmen are highly revered by their units. Marines, soldiers, sailors, airmen, and coasties all know that their "doc" may save their life. They are to be protected at all costs. Their heroism is frequently without parallel. Ask anybody who's been in combat, and they'll tell you how their doc risked his own life to save somebody else's. Many docs

I've talked to say "I was just doing my job." True, but they usually go above and beyond, without any thought to their own safety. Their humility is usually overwhelming. I'm always shocked at their surprise when I tell them they're considered to be the "rock stars" of the military and how much they're admired. They usually just say things like "I was just doing my job."

Medevac, Baghdad, Iraq, 2004, Dept. of Defense

Another reason most people admire and respect them so much, is that we know they have an extra burden to carry. They have acted as a wounded or dying person's mother, father, priest, and friend. They have had to be responsible for people's lives in the chaos of combat. They have been put in the position of having to alleviate a person's pain or make their death more peaceful. That is a burden few of us are prepared to handle. They have had to hear the unbearable questions like "Why me doc?" or "Am I going to die?" They have had to lie to their patients to try to provide comfort and consolation in their hour of need. "You'll be okay soldier, just hang in there with me," as they watch the person take their last breath. One

Operation Hue City, Vietnam, 1967, National Archives

corpsman said that he had to have "compassion wrapped in steel" to make the difficult decisions sometimes of who would live or die, given limited resources or time in emergencies.

Nobody should have to bear that kind of burden. Unfortunately, war requires that role be filled, and usually by relatively young people. How is an eighteen year old, with six to twelve weeks of training and no combat experience, supposed to save lives like a trauma surgeon in a fully equipped hospital? Trauma physicians go through many years of specialized training and are closely supervised while they perfect their skills. They have the latest equipment and plenty of support staff to assist them. Not so with docs in the field or primitive aid stations. Somehow these young docs are supposed to perform miracles, which somehow they seem to do with

Operation Dewey Canyon, Vietnam, 1969, National Archives

some degree of regularity. Yet, somehow the guilt always remains.

Most docs I've spoken to are very hard on themselves. They seem to remember the people they lost or the mistakes they made more than they ever think about all the lives they saved. They hold themselves to impossibly high standards. They took their jobs seriously and expected perfection from themselves. Anything less than perfection could cost lives and was unacceptable. It's an impossible situation to be in. Many carry the guilt of having been wounded themselves. They feel they let their troops down by getting wounded and having to be taken out by medevac themselves. They feel they have abandoned their people and let them down. Even when

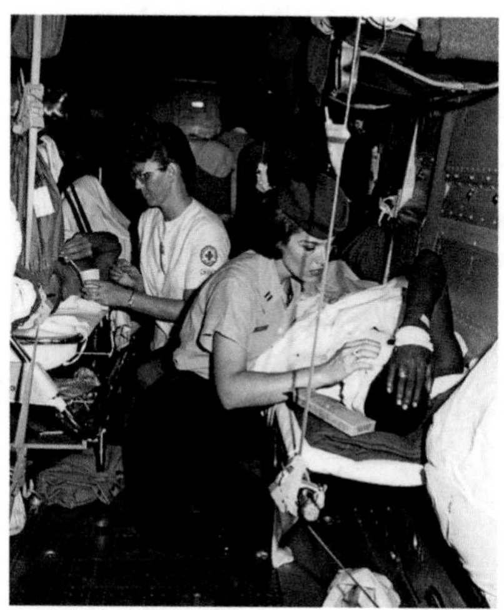

Flight nurses in Vietnam, National Archives

they themselves are wounded, they are still selflessly worried about those they are supposed to be caring for.

How many times has a medic or corpsman had to put one of their patients on a chopper, never to know if they lived or died. How do you deal with unfinished business like that? Many try to assume that they did their job of stabilizing the patient to the best of their ability. If they're lucky, they can make the assumption that their patients made it. Usually, though, they have a fairly good idea of who would make it and who wouldn't. Now, that's real unfinished business. I don't think there are any eighteen to twenty one year olds really emotionally equipped to handle those kinds of burdens. Frankly, I don't think it's easy for a doc of any age or degree of life experience. Yet, they accept the burden and risk their lives and live with the guilt and unfinished business. So, next time you see a doc, make sure to give them a special, heartfelt thank you for their service. That goes for the nurses, doctors, x-ray techs, and other healthcare providers in the war zone.

The special thank you list would certainly not be complete if we didn't also mention the helicopter pilots who got the wounded out by medevac. They usually risked their lives against unbeatable odds to come in and

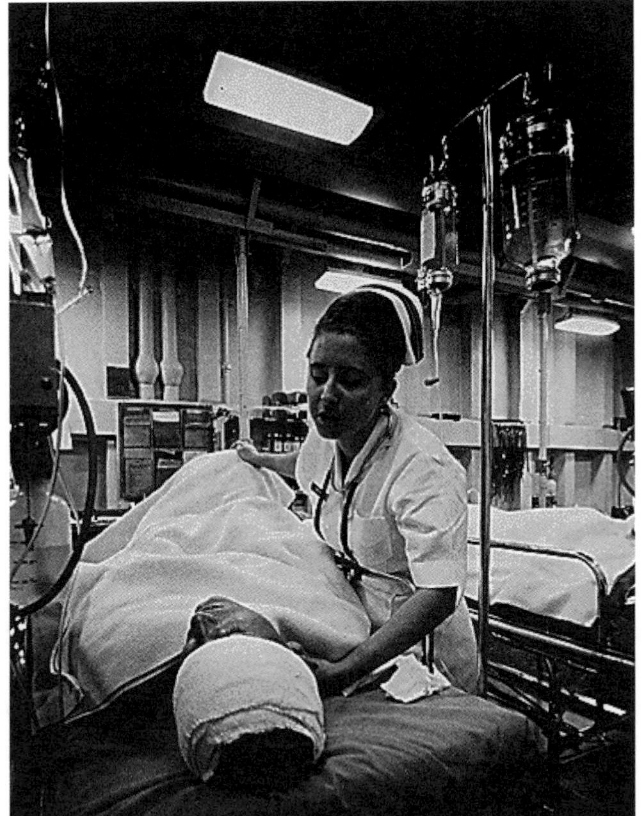

Nurse in Vietnam, National Archives

pick up their wounded comrades. After having spoken with many chopper pilots, they carry a huge burden as well. They speak of the times they tried to get in to pick up the wounded and just couldn't. They talk about how hard it is to leave the people behind when they're over their weight limits. They frequently deal with the guilt of having to leave warriors in desperate situations against insurmountable numbers of the enemy. Many of these pilots have gone above and beyond the call of duty to come back and pick up their own. Don't forget to give them an extra thanks as well.

EOD folks are also in a league of their own. Many of you have probably seen the movie which came out recently portraying what that experience is like. Movies don't ever completely capture the experiences, especially

Khe Sahn, Vietnam, 1968, Robert Ellison/Empire News

when it comes to war. It does give you pause to consider the extra burden and risk they take on every time they perform their job. Many people did mine sweeps, demolitions, and were intimately involved with explosives in previous wars without that special title. Those people carried just as much of a burden as they do nowadays. Give them a special thank you too.

EOD, Dept. of Defense

Chapter Twenty One

From Hero to Zero

Speaking of giving people a special thank you for their service… Many who came home from Vietnam were greeted by protesters and insults. Many were spit on and called "baby killers." That's no way for a nation to welcome home it's warriors. After having served their country, they were treated disrespectfully when they came home. This was a huge betrayal on the part of the very country they served. It was very painful and frequently devastating, particularly after they saw their buddies lose their lives. Many Vietnam veterans got into fights, became bitter or ashamed, or totally withdrew from society as a result of the way they were treated when they came home. Can't blame them either.

Even today, because of various political beliefs, people will say insulting things to our warriors when they return. I know a veteran who returned from several tours in Iraq. I've heard of people asking current active duty or reserve folks things like "How can you people sleep at night? You're baby killers." One guy's response I heard to this was, "It's okay, we only kill what we eat." Needless to say, that usually leaves them pretty much speechless. Don't buy into the criticism somebody heaps on you or the negative judgments somebody passes on you. If they weren't there, then they don't have a right to criticize you. Please know that there are many Americans who support our troops from today's wars and wars in the past.

What does somebody expect when they come home after they've been through hell serving their country in a war zone? They certainly don't expect to be insulted, rejected, criticized, or mocked. Especially after they've seen people pay the ultimate price and sacrifice of their life in the line of duty. It's especially infuriating when the person making the nasty remarks hasn't experienced what you have and hasn't been there to see it with their own eyes. They're basing their decisions and reactions on what some of the news media has portrayed or their friends' political opinions.

Operations Hastings, Dong Ha, Vietnam, 1966, National Archives

I've heard guys say they went "from a hero over there to a zero here" when they got back home. They were a good soldier, marine, sailor, or airman and did their job to the best of their ability. They risked their lives and saw others give theirs. You're still basically the same person you were over there. So what changed from the time you got on the plane over there until you got off the plane over here? Nothing really. It's the politics and viewpoints of those here which have changed. Even if people don't support the politics of the war, it's the individual veterans who deserve our respect and thanks. Most of you weren't expecting a ticker-tape parade like some of the WW II veterans got. But maybe a little gratefulness on the part of the nation you were fighting for would be nice. But at the very least you shouldn't be denigrated, insulted, rejected, or shunned for doing your jobs.

I read a letter once written by a marine serving in Iraq. He said he wanted to personally thank every Vietnam veteran he met. He said they are the reason the current troops are receiving so much public support, care packages, and being welcomed home at airports. He said the United States learned a shameful lesson about how to treat it's warriors after Vietnam. He said the nation had realized it's mistakes in treating the individual warriors so disgracefully. He felt the country had learned a painful lesson and was now treating it's warriors the way it always should have.

Vietnam War Memorial, Washington, D.C., Author's collection

Whether something is called a war or a police action or a conflict, it's just semantics and labels when it comes down to it. If young men and women are fighting against an enemy and getting wounded or dying as a result of it, then it's war. Leave the political definitions to the politicians. The devastating effects on individuals and families is the same. Anybody who goes into a battlefield comes out wounded and changed in some fashion. It may be their values, beliefs about the world, their own identify, their spiritual beliefs, their morals, their sense of what safety is, what they perceive as the purpose or meaning of life. All of these things, and many more, can be deeply affected by the experiences in a war zone or on the battlefield. Almost every war veteran experiences Post Combat Reaction (PCR) to one degree or another.

Desert Storm, leaving Kuwait, 1991, Dept. of Defense

I've heard guys who were in Vietnam say they were turned away from veteran's organizations here in the states when they first got back. I've heard cases of other military personnel criticizing and insulting those who were in Iraq, Afghanistan, Panama, Kosovo, Bosnia, Somalia, Nicaragua, and other places. If you don't agree with the politics, then say that and have an adult discussion about it, but don't pass judgment on the individual who went because his government sent him or her. One guy I know compared it to Enron. He said it's fine to go ahead and criticize the CEO's and people who were making the decisions over there. But don't hold it personally against the janitor and the receptionist. They most likely don't have any idea what's going on at the top of the heap. They're doing their job the best way they know how to support their family. Obviously I'm not talking about people who knowingly commit crimes or atrocities, only to then say they were only doing what they were told. I'm talking about the regular Joe who does his best to stay alive and keep his/her buddies alive too.

If somebody comes up to you and says "thank you for your service," it can be awkward or even embarrassing at times. However, most people who say that are genuine in their expression of gratitude. The public is becoming more aware of the toll taken on warriors and their families. That's a good thing. So accept their thanks graciously and realize what a gift it is. The nation is finally understanding the debt we owe to our warriors and their families, so let them express their appreciation. Those who fought in Vietnam were deprived of that. It's time to right that wrong.

CHAPTER TWENTY TWO

Improvise, Adapt and Overcome

Resilience. That's a subject which counselors talk about a lot in reference to people who have been through war. My understanding of the term, in that context, is that it means the traumatic experiences can make you stronger and cause you to develop new strengths. The analogy I like to use is comparing the warrior to a sword. They used to make swords by taking the steel and heating it over the fire and pounding it, making the steel denser and stronger. War can have that effect on people too. You have all heard the expression "That which does not kill me makes me stronger." If that's what they mean by resilience which is developed as a result of war, then I guess that's true.

WW II, First flag on Guam, 1944, National Archives

Anybody who's been in a war zone doesn't usually get shaken to their core very easily later on in their lives. You're the ones who don't get shaken up in an emergency situation. You react immediately and take care of the situation without getting emotional or upset. You can get through any crisis, and I do mean any. Adapt, improvise, and overcome.

Afghanistan, 2004, Dept. of Defense

That's why so many people turn to you when there's a problem to solve at home or at work. You are a natural leader as a result of your experiences. You know how to take charge of a situation and do whatever needs to be done. You're used to making sure your people are taken care of, particularly if you've been in any kind of leadership position in a war zone. It really is a matter of life or death sometimes. That's why you're always prepared and step up to take charge of a situation if other people don't. The good news is that you're good at it and always get the job done efficiently. The bad news is that once people find out you're good at it, they are likely to look to you even more in the future. That can make for a lot of extra responsibility. Just because you're good at handling responsibility efficiently, doesn't make it any less heavy of a burden. It still drains resources and energy from other things.

Since you're usually the one taking responsibility for other people, it's easy to forget about taking care of yourself and your own needs. Part of the healing process requires that you begin to pay attention to the wear and tear you've experienced as a result of your war experiences. War takes its toll on all those involved, military and civilians. It takes its toll on you and your family. It is imperative that you begin to recognize your own needs. Pay attention to your physical, psychological, and spiritual needs. Talking to a counselor or chaplain can help in this area. If you are taking care of a lot of other people,

Preparing for a mission, Iraq, 2010, Dept. of Defense

maybe it's time to circle the wagons and focus more on your own health. This is particularly true in today's economy when many people are struggling financially. It's great to help other people when you have the surplus to spare. However, if you've been feeling more exhausted or stressed, physically, financially, or mentally, you have to evaluate your priorities. Adjust them accordingly. Anything you're doing which is not of critical importance to your own, or your family's well-being, should probably be put on hold for the time being.

Combat veterans have had to push above and beyond. They are usually capable of accomplishing whatever goals they put their minds to. They've learned persistence, endurance, and commitment from their experiences in war. It makes you think you have an unlimited amount of internal strength and energy. Unfortunately, as we get older, we begin to realize that our internal resources are a limited commodity. We can't do the same things we used to be able to when we were 18 or 20 years old. Our bodies and our minds won't let us. Hopefully, as we mature, we can recognize that we have to work smarter, not harder. We have to learn to be more proactive in allocating our resources. We have to pay closer attention to our priorities and how we spend our energy. Somebody very wise (my father) once told me "Your time, energy, and money are all limited resources, so use them wisely." Good advice, so take a look at how you spend each one of them and make sure it's the way you want it to be.

Chapter Twenty Three

"I'm From The Government And I'm Here To Help"

Actually, this book is in no way affiliated with the Veteran's Administration, Department of Defense, or any branch of the military. However, the V.A. can help you. There are some who may have had less than wonderful experiences in dealing with military healthcare systems in the past. The system has greatly improved and now realizes that veterans are the customers, without whom government employees would not have jobs. There are avenues to pursue if you're not happy with the services you are receiving. It's definitely worth a try if you are interested in getting assistance in coping with life after war.

If you've been diagnosed with PTSD and were in the military, please at least check out what's available at your local V.A. If you went and had a bad experience in the past, don't give up, because it's changed for the better. No organization is perfect, but the "customer service oriented" approach has definitely arrived at most V.A.'s. If you go to one and don't like the specific provider there, then request another one if possible. If you don't like the facility, then go to another facility. Nowadays there are V.A. clinics near most cities, even some of the smaller ones. Without you, the veteran, there are no customers and no jobs. That fact isn't lost on the new and improved Veteran's Administration. I'm just sayin'...

You'll notice I haven't really used the term PTSD, or post-traumatic stress disorder, so far in this book. There are several reasons for that. One, is that the symptoms of PTSD, are usually experienced to one degree or another by most people who have been to war. That's because many of the reactions are natural reactions to unnatural, traumatic experiences. So, the "disorder" part isn't always appropriate for all people. This is why I'm proposing that we use the term Post Combat Reaction (PCR) to describe the natural reactions that most people have after returning from war. The term Post Combat Reaction (PCR) is appropriate for the majority of returning veterans who have the symptoms or reactions, but do not have them severely enough to be diagnosed with full-blown PTSD.

The second reason I haven't used that term, is that this label of PTSD can have a stigma associated with it. That probably comes from the old days when the media portrayed war veterans with PTSD as crazy, violent, bad-asses. Truth be told, most of the guys who were living with these issues back then didn't really talk about it to anybody. They came back from the war, in Europe, the Pacific, Korea, Vietnam, or wherever, and went about trying to do the best they could. Most of those guys just figured that this was their own personal reaction so they had to just "suck it up and carry on" in true military tradition. In those days, many viewed talking about the psychological effects of war as "whining" or" weak" or "unmanly." The third reason I haven't used the term, is that it can be interpreted as meaning there's something "wrong" with somebody, that they're defective in some way for feeling or reacting the way they do.

Well, I'm here to tell you that most of the guys I've talked to that have been diagnosed with PTSD are some of the strongest, bravest people I have ever met. It's not an inherent weakness or defect in a person. There are a lot of factors that can put people at risk for developing PTSD. Recent research is finding more evidence that there are certain genetic or biological components that make certain people more likely to develop PTSD than others. Another factor that affects whether somebody will develop it is the amount of trauma they've already had in their life prior to their war experiences. It makes sense that if you've already got a bunch of stress and trauma piled on top of you at a young age, you're at more risk even before you get exposed to the war-related trauma. It has a cumulative effect. It just keeps building up on top of what was already there.

There are several factors associated with traumatic war experiences that also put a person at risk. The more levels of vulnerability you have at the time of the trauma can make you more at risk. For example, if you don't have enough ammo, or food and water, or troop support, you're more likely to experience the situation as even more traumatic. If you don't have what you need to get the job done, the experience of helplessness, or of being overwhelmed, just adds to the trauma. Just think of the medic or corpsman who doesn't have enough morphine or bandages or training or experience. That's the classic no-win situation. You're set up to be even more overwhelmed with helpless feelings than you would be if you had everything you needed to get the job done. You can see how it complicates an already traumatic situation. How soon you are exposed to trauma after arriving in the war zone can also be a risk factor for developing PTSD. If somebody experiences a particularly horrific event right after they arrived in the war zone, it sets the stage for the rest of their time there. If they've been traumatized before they even got their feet firmly on the ground, then they haven't even had a chance to acclimate to their new surroundings and get the lay of the land. It can set them up for being more easily traumatized again if they haven't formed their emotional callouses and coping skills yet.

If you grew up in a military family where a parent had PTSD, you may have been more at risk for developing it yourself. If your father or grandfather was a combat veteran, they may have had PTSD or some of the symptoms. You may have been influenced by watching the way they coped with those symptoms. Perhaps they were angry a lot, or hypervigilant, or emotionally detached. PTSD can be handed down across generations, just like many other family traits or traditions. Not only might there be a genetic component to PTSD, there can also be an environmental factor. For example, you may have learned that men don't cry or talk about their feelings or negative experiences. You may have learned valuable coping skills, like being able to suck it up and carry on. These are important coping skills that help people deal with the traumas of war. Coping skills which develop in the face of trauma only become negative if they interfere with your relationships and happiness. Having watched a parent with PTSD while you were growing up may actually have helped you understand your own experiences better. It may have helped you feel that you are not alone, and that there is a valid reason for your feelings and reactions. Hopefully you can begin a dialogue with your parent or child about the role of PTSD in your relationship over the years. Ideally, you can communicate the universal nature of many of the reactions and coping skills people develop to cope with war. There is no shame in speaking the truth. Usually talking about the pain of war ends up helping to bridge the silence and the gap between the generations.

So, you can see that developing PTSD is really nothing to be ashamed of. Certain people are just naturally more at risk than others. If you have been diagnosed with PTSD, please don't look at yourself as weak or defective. It is what it is. It's more of a reflection on the severity of the traumas you've been exposed to than a reflection of your own personal character. Like I've said many times before, almost all people who have been in combat experience some degree of the symptoms of PTSD. This is why it's important to have a term like Post Combat Reaction to describe the normal reactions of the majority of war veterans.

For those of you who are wondering what post-traumatic stress disorder (PTSD) is, I wanted to give you the definition and symptoms. According to the DSM-IV, which is the Diagnostic and Statistical Manual Fourth Edition, there are certain criteria which a person has to meet before achieving the diagnosis of PTSD. The DSM-IV is the diagnostic manual used by those of us in the field of mental health so we have standardized guidelines and definitions for various psychiatric and psychological disorders. As this book goes to press they are working on the next 5th edition, estimated to come out in 2013. Only a mental health professional can make a diagnosis of PTSD. If you suspect you might be experiencing symptoms of PTSD, please consult a mental health professional. This book is not meant to be a substitute for medical opinions and advice, nor is it considered to be a treatment. This information is being provided for informational and educational purposes only.

Anybody can experience PTSD. It can be a civilian who is raped or assaulted or in a bad car accident. It can be somebody who's been to war or in a natural disaster. One of the main requirements is that the person has to have experienced, witnessed, or have been confronted with an event that involved either threatened or actual death, serious injury, or threat to the physical integrity of themselves or somebody else. In other words, you believe your own life or somebody else's to be in danger. The second main requirement is that the person feels an intense fear, horror, or sense of helplessness. In other words, they have to actually feel traumatized by what they're seeing or experiencing. When an experience involves both of these things, it is considered traumatic enough to result in PTSD.

Experiencing a combination of these things does not automatically result in PTSD. Many times people will experience a trauma and have symptoms of PTSD or combat operational stress initially. If there has only been one trauma and the person has time to heal and recover, then the symptoms will often fade. As long as the symptoms last only for about a month or so, this is referred to as an acute stress reaction. This is quite natural for most people who have experienced a traumatic event. If the trauma is singular and the person is safe afterwards, and able to begin the natural healing process, then the symptoms will likely resolve themselves.

War zones and combat typically involve either repeated traumatic experiences or ongoing feelings of danger and vulnerability. When this is the case, it's harder for the natural healing to begin. If you're worried about getting killed, it's pretty hard to start processing what just happened to you and begin to make sense of it. This delay in the healing process is what can result in PTSD.

Sometimes the symptoms of PTSD don't always surface immediately after a traumatic experience. At times there can be a delay in the onset. It can seem as if the person is numb or in shock or denial for some period after the trauma. Sometimes this is the case. Everybody experiences their reactions in a different way. If a person experiences the symptoms of PTSD for at least a month up until about three months or so, then that is referred to as acute PTSD. However, if the symptoms last longer than three months, this is considered to be more chronic. There is no specific time line for the way an individual reacts after a trauma. These are only ways of differentiating between types of PTSD.

The symptoms of PTSD involve three general groups. These are re-experiencing, arousal, and avoidance. Re-experiencing a trauma can appear in several different ways. Typically these might occur as intrusive memories or nightmares about the event. Sometimes a person can actually feel as if the traumatic event was occurring again. In other words, they feel as if they are reliving it. These are referred to as flashbacks. A person can experience intense emotional or physical reactions to things that remind them of the trauma.

Arousal can mean when a person becomes either emotionally or physically agitated or upset when exposed to something which reminds the person about the trauma. We usually call those "triggers." Arousal can be experienced either psychologically, physically, or both. Sometimes people find they are hypervigilant and react strongly to loud noises or unexpected movements. Sometimes they have difficulty getting to sleep or wake up a lot. If you've had to sleep with one eye open in a war zone, then you might sleep so lightly that you wake up a lot. Other times people find themselves very irritable or have angry outbursts which might be more of a reaction than what the situation deserves. If you're feeling very tense or irritable or not sleeping well, this can interfere with your ability to concentrate as well.

Avoidance of triggers associated with the trauma are typically an effort to avoid the emotional pain they cause. Avoidance of reminders of the trauma also serve to prevent an increase in the painful memories. Sometimes people avoided registering the details of the trauma as it occurred. They might have mentally "checked out," during the trauma. This can result in what is called dissociation. Their body was there, but their mind was not fully present. Many people avoid activities they used to enjoy prior to the traumatic experience. Some feel very emotionally detached and numb in an effort to avoid getting close to other people. This can be a self-protective coping skill in some cases. Once a person's life has been in danger, particularly if they feel they escaped death, they might have a feeling that they may not live as long as other people. In other words, if they've cheated death once already, they wonder how long their luck will hold out.

If somebody experiences a significant number of the reactions described above they may be experiencing PTSD. These may result in difficulties with their personal relationships, work, and social functioning. Only a mental health professional can make an accurate diagnosis of PTSD.

Combat operational stress reaction is a term

sometimes used while still deployed. This is typically used to describe common reactions which most troops experience at some time or another while in theatre. It usually refers to reactions such as being on edge all the time, increased irritability, difficulty sleeping, being keyed up and jumpy. Quite frankly, given the job and the living conditions can you blame a person? I think it kind of goes with the territory.

If you're concerned that you might have PTSD, please go to the V.A. or talk to your health care provider about your concerns and symptoms. Believe me, you are definitely not alone. Estimates of the number of combat veterans experiencing PTSD now have ranged from 10-30% of those deployed to a war zone. There is no shame in acknowledging the toll which war has taken on you. The main thing is to get back on top of your game and be able to live a healthier and happier life. If you won't get help for your own sake, do it for the people you love.

CHAPTER TWENTY FOUR

After Action Report

The healing begins when you realize that what you're thinking and feeling is natural, given what you've lived through in the war zone. Once you understand why you feel and act the way you do, hopefully there's some sense of relief. A degree of relief in knowing that you're not "going crazy". The more you know about the effects of war, the better you'll be able to understand your own reactions. Then, hopefully you can explain them better to your family members. Another important factor in the healing process is realizing that you're not alone. Everybody who's been in combat experiences some degree of the issues talked about in this book. Not everybody will experience all of them. Some people will have all of them. How strongly you identify with these effects of war will vary a lot.

The more combat exposure and life threatening situations you experienced typically results in more intense experiences afterwards. Makes sense. The more trauma you experience, the more intense the emotional and psychological effects afterwards.

The course of the healing process varies for everybody and there is no set time frame. Everybody recovers from the effects of war at their own pace. So, if anybody tells you it's time to "just get over it already," tell them it doesn't work that way. It takes as long as it takes. Many combat veterans who have never fully understood the effects of war have been walking around with a huge burden for thirty years or more. This is only because they never had the opportunity to learn about or work through some of their experiences or reactions. However, once they do begin the process there is usually overall improvement in their symptoms and in personal growth.

Usually the recovery process has a lot of ups and downs, particularly at the beginning. Sometimes it may seem as though you go two steps forward and then three steps back. But I can tell you from a lot of experience, that in most cases, there is steady improvement overall. It's important if you experience a setback, not to get too down on yourself, or think you're back to square one. It can be a bit of a roller coaster, but remain hopeful and don't give up.

We can't erase what happened. You will never forget what you experienced. You probably wouldn't want to forget out of respect for the lives which were lost. However, it is definitely possible to get to the point where some of the painful memories aren't in your face all the time. You can get to the point where they're more off into your peripheral vision, or the back burner.

You can learn to get better control over your temper. You can learn how to recognize and avoid your triggers. You can train yourself to relax a little bit and not be quite so "on edge" all the time. You can learn ways of communicating better with your loved one so that your relationships can actually grow as a result of the hardships you've all experienced. There are many, many combat veterans who are thinking and feeling the same things you are. They just don't talk about it, just like you probably don't.

It's time to break the silence and speak the truth. War is hell, and part of that hell is dealing with the after effects which most veterans and their families live with. The more we talk about the common experiences which combat veterans share, Post Combat Reaction, the more we can eliminate the stigma. Freedom is not free. We have to start someplace, so I hope this book will help accomplish that goal in some small way. Welcome home and thank you for your service.

Afghanistan, 2010, Dept. of Defense

Resources

General Resources:

Military One Source for military personnel, spouses, and families 1.800.342.9647
http://www.militaryonesource.com/

United States Department of Veterans Affairs
http://www.va.gov/

Federal and military resources
http://www.realwarriors.net/partner/federalmilitary.php

OEF/OIF veterans
http://www.oefoif.va.gov/

Iraq and Afghanistan Veterans of America (IAVA)
http://iava.org/

Vietnam Veterans of America (VVA)
http://www.vva.org/

Women veterans
http://www.mentalhealth.va.gov/womenvets.asp

Vet centers locations
http://www2.va.gov/directory/guide/vetcenter_flsh.asp

Veteran's Health Administration, facility locations
http://www.va.gov/landing2_locations.htm

Veteran's Benefits Administration, facility location
http://www.va.gov/landing2_locations.htm

Veteran's service organizations, suicide prevention resources, consumer organizations, and professional organizations
http://www.mentalhealth.va.gov/Resources.asp

Post Deployment:

After deployment wellness resources
http://www.afterdeployment.org/

Deployment health clinical center: post-deployment health
http://www.pdhealth.mil/

Post-Deployment Health Reassessment (PDHRA) Program
http://www.pdhealth.mil/dcs/pdhra.asp

Yellow Ribbon Project for National Guard and Reserves
http://www.yellowribbon.mil

Returning veterans
http://www.mentalhealth.va.gov/returningservicevets.asp

Resilience, recovery, reintegration
http://www.realwarriors.net/

Wounded Warriors:

Wounded Warriors Project
https://www.woundedwarriorproject.org/

Marines Wounded Warriors
http://www.woundedwarriorregiment.org/

Army Wounded Warriors
http://www.aw2.army.mil/

Air Force Wounded Warriors
http://www.woundedwarrior.af.mil/

Mental Health Resources:

National Center for PTSD
http://www.ptsd.va.gov/

PTSD information
http://www.mentalhealth.va.gov/PTSD.asp

VA Mental Health
http://www.mentalhealth.va.gov/VAMentalHealthGroup.asp

Defense center of excellence for psychological health and traumatic brain injury
http://www.dcoe.health.mil/

Depression
http://www.mentalhealth.va.gov/depression.asp

Substance abuse
http://www.mentalhealth.va.gov/substanceabuse.asp

Suicide prevention
http://www.suicidepreventionlifeline.org/

Suicide prevention
http://www.mentalhealth.va.gov/suicide_prevention/

Military sexual trauma
http://www.mentalhealth.va.gov/msthome.asp

Marines Combat Operational Stress Control
http://www.usmc-mccs.org/cosc/

Work, School, and Home:

Vocational rehabilitation and employment
http://www.vba.va.gov/bln/vre/

America's Heroes at work
http://www.americasheroesatwork.gov/

Veterans at work
http://www.mentalhealth.va.gov/vetsatwork.asp

Student veterans
http://www.mentalhealth.va.gov/College/veteranfamilies.asp

Student veterans' organization
http://www.studentveterans.org/

Homelessness
http://www.mentalhealth.va.gov/homelessness.asp

Self Help Guides:

After the War Zone: A Practical Guide for Returning Troops and Their Families. Laurie B. Slone, Ph.D. and Matthew Friedman, MD, Ph.D. Philadelphia: Da Capo Press, 2008.

The Anger Control Workbook. Matthew McKay, Ph.D., and Peter Rogers, Ph.D. CA: New Harbinger Publications, 2000.

Back From the Front: Combat Trauma, Love, and the Family. Aphrodite Matsakis, Ph.D. MD: Sidran Institute Press, 2007

Conquering Post-Traumatic Stress Disorder. Victoria Lemle Beckner, Ph.D. and John B. Arden, Ph.D. MA: Fair Winds Press, 2008.

Courage After Fire: Coping Strategies for Troops Returning from Iraq and Afghanistan and Their Families. Keith Armstrong, L.C.S.W., Suzanne Best, Ph.D. and Paula Domenici, Ph.D. CA: Ulysses Press, 2006.

Down Range to Iraq and Back. Bridget C. Cantrell, Ph.D. and Chuck Dean. WA: WordSmith Books, 2005.

Once a Warrior Always a Warrior: Navigating the Transition from Combat to Home. Charles W. Hoge, M.D. CT: Globe Pequot Press, 2010.

The PTSD Workbook. Mary Beth Willliams, Ph.D., L.C.S.W., C.T.S. and Soili Poijula, Ph.D. CA: NewHarbinger Publications, 2000.

Additional Reading:

Achilles in Vietnam: Combat Trauma and the Undoing of Character. Jonathan Shay, M.D., Ph.D. NY: Scribner, 1994.

Haunted by Combat: Understanding PTSD in War Veterans Including Women, Reservists, and Those Coming Back from Iraq. Darryl S. Paulson and Stanley Krippner. CT: Praeger Security International,2007.

Odysseus in America: Combat Trauma and the Trials of Homecoming. Jonathan Shay, M.D., Ph.D. NY: Scribner, 2002.

On Combat. Grossman, Dave and Loren Christensen. Warrior Science Publications., 2004

On Killing. Grossman, Dave. New York: Back Bay Books, 1995

Rule Number Two: Lessons I Learned in a Combat Hospital. Heidi Squier Kraft, Ph.D. New York: Hachette Book Group USA, 2007.

Trained to Kill: Soldiers at War. Theodore Nadelson, M.A., M.D. MD: Johns Hopkins University Press, 2005.

Vietnam Wives: Women and Children Surviving Life with Veterans Suffering Post-Traumatic Stress Disorder. Aphrodite Matsakis, Ph.D. Woodbine House, 1988.

REFERENCES

Grossman, Dave and Loren Christensen. *On Combat.* Warrior Science Publications., 2004

Grossman, Dave. *On Killing.* New York: Back Bay Books, 1995

Abbreviations:

AIT: Advanced Infantry Training or Advanced Individual Training

Black ops: Black operations, covert operations

CPAP machine: Continuous Positive Airway Pressure to treat sleep apnea

C-rations: Individual canned rations meal

DMZ: Demilitarized Zone

DSM-IV: Diagnostic and Statistical Manual of Mental Disorders, 4th Edition

EOD: Explosive Ordnance Disposal

FOB: Forward Operating Base

IED: Improvised Explosive Device

Intel: Intelligence information

Medevac: Medical evacuation

MRE: Meal, ready to eat

PCR: Post Combat Reaction

PTSD: Post Traumatic Stress Disorder

R and R: Rest and relaxation

SSRI: Selective serotonin re-uptake inhibitor anti-depressant

VA: Veteran's Administration

INDEX

About the Author

Anne Freund, Ph.D. is a licensed clinical psychologist who has been practicing since 1989. She graduated from Duke University with a Bachelor's in Psychology and from the University of Florida with a Ph.D. in Clinical Psychology. Dr. Freund completed her internship at the VA in Bay Pines, FL. She has been with the Department of Veterans Affairs since 2005. Prior to that she worked with law enforcement and first responders as part of a Critical Incidence Stress Debriefing Team. Dr. Freund began conducting PTSD support groups in 2005, shortly after arriving at the VA. She has had specialized training in PTSD at the National Center for PTSD in Menlo Park, California and at the Center for Deployment Psychology at the Uniformed Services University of the Health Sciences in Bethesda, Maryland. Dr Freund is a member of the American Psychological Association, the International Society for Traumatic Stress, European Society for Stress Studies, the Association of VA Psychologist Leaders, and the American Academy of Experts in Traumatic Stress.